C000072205

GCSE
Textiles Technology
for OCR

Carey Clarkson, Jayne March, Joy Palmer

Heinemann Educational Publishers
Halley Court, Jordan Hill, Oxford OX2 8EJ
Part of Harcourt Education

Heinemann is the registered trademark of
Harcourt Education Limited

Text © Carey Clarkson, Jayne March, Joy Palmer, 2002

First published in 2002

06 05 04 03
10 9 8 7 6 5 4 3

All rights reserved.

Apart from any fair dealing for the purposes of
research or private study, or criticism or review as
permitted under the terms of the UK Copyright,
Designs and Patents Act 1988, this publication may
not be reproduced, stored or transmitted, in any form
or by any means, without the prior permission in
writing of the publishers, or in the case of
reprographic reproduction only in accordance with
the terms of the licences issued by the Copyright
Licensing Agency in the UK, or in accordance with the
terms of licences issued by the appropriate
Reproduction Rights Organization outside the UK.
Enquiries concerning reproduction outside the terms
stated here should be sent to the publishers at the
address printed on this page.

British Library Cataloguing in Publication Data
A catalogue record for this book is available from the
British Library.

ISBN 0 435 41666 9

Typeset by Artistix, Thame, Oxon.
Illustrations by Mike Atkinson and Jim Eldridge.
Original illustrations © Heinemann Educational
Publishers 2002.
Printed and bound in Spain by Edelvives.

Acknowledgements
This book has been developed with the support of
OCR. Thank you to John Hill for his guidance. The
authors would also like to thank all the students who
have contributed examples of their work, particularly
Louise Barker, Hayley Brotherston, Justine Chapman
(Designing tips), Victoria Clarke, Lotte Gjertson,
Rebecca Kearney, Lucy McQuillan, Sara McDonald,
Rebecca Melton, Gemma Robinson, Kirsteen Rodger
and Sara Waters from Nunthorpe School in
Middlesborough. Thanks also to Holmesdale
Technology College in Kent. Thanks to Jonathan
Wragg and Barbara Eia, who helped with the initial
word-processing and Vicky Liu and the Hartlepool
Sewing Centre for providing fabric samples.

The publishers would like to thank Steiff for the 2001
Bear Concept on p.36 and Dyson for the image of the
washing machine on p.72.

The publishers would like to thank the following for
permission to use photographs:
Art Directors/Trip p.61, 77 (top right); Cloth of Gold
p.86 (left), 111; Empics p.63 (top); Eye Ubiquitous
p.132; Husqvarna p.83; John Lewis p.88 (both);
Martindale p.64; Mountain Camera Picture Research
Library/John Cleare 60 (right); Yiorgos Nikiteas p.7, 13
(top), 16 (both), 20 (left), 30, 43, 46 (bottom right), 48
(top), 54, 55, 58 (bottom), 62 (right), 74, 76 (bottom
left and top right), 85, 87, 89 (both), 112, 113, 120
(all), 135, 150, 151, 152 (both), 154 (both), 155;
PYMCA/Henry Iddon p.22; Paxar p.25 (all); Powerstock
p.63 (bottom); Replin p.60 (left); Retna p.13 (bottom),
19, 34, 76 (bottom right), 77 (top left and bottom
right), 103 (both), 106 (bottom left, bottom right);
Rimoldi p.118; Science Photo Library p.47, 48 (bottom
left), 91 (right); Science Photo Library/RE Litchfield
p.59; SDL International Ltd p.68; Textiles Magazine
(issue 3) p.57; Tony Stone p.47 (right), 62 (left), 91
(left); Trip/Grant 86 (right); Trip/Kolpakov p.20
(right); Wacom p.41; ZSK p.83 (tubular system
machine), 106 (top right).

The publishers have made every effort to contact
copyright holders. However, if any material has been
incorrectly acknowledged, the publishers would be
pleased to correct this at the earliest opportunity.

Tel: 01865 888058 www.heinemann.co.uk

Contents

Introduction

This book has been written to meet the specification requirements for the OCR GCSE in Design and Technology (D&T): Textiles Technology. The book covers all the requirements for the short and full course; extra material and exemplification is contained within the Teacher's Resource File. The OCR specification is designed to meet the National Curriculum Orders for D&T and the GCSE Subject Criteria for D&T.

The programme of study for D&T at Key Stage 4 requires you to develop your D&T capability by applying knowledge and understanding when developing ideas, planning, making products and evaluating products.

The OCR specification content provides opportunities for you to develop D&T capability through activities, including:

- product analysis
- focused practical tasks that develop a range of techniques, skills, processes and knowledge
- 'design and make' assignments, which include activities related to industrial practices and the application of systems and control.

You will be assessed in two ways. You will have internal assessment on your coursework (for up to 60% of the marks). You will also have to do a written examination at the end of the course (for up to 40% of the marks).

How to use the book

The book is divided into the following parts:

- Developing a design brief and drawing up a specification
- Generating design proposals
- Product development
- Product planning and realization
- Product evaluation
- Internal assessment and post-GCSE options.

Within each of these parts, the knowledge and understanding of Textiles Technology is covered, as well as help and advice on internal assessment objectives (coursework). ICT, industrial practice and health and safety are also covered.

The book is written in a series of double-page spreads which include:

- specification links – these show which sections of the specification are covered by the spread
- activities – these test knowledge and understanding and can be used in independent study and for revision
- key points – these provide a summary of some of the most important points on the spread and will be useful for revision.

Symbols are used on the spreads to show work covering ICT and industrial practice:

   indicates ICT

   indicates industrial practice.

At the end of each part, there is a set of more detailed questions that test your knowledge and understanding of the specification content.

The book is supported by a Teacher's Resource File, which provides more information on certain topics and proformas for coursework. When extra material is provided in the Teacher's Resource File, this is shown by the symbol:
Your teacher will let you have the sheets you need.

Textiles Technology is an ever-changing subject and, as a result, many types of resource are needed to provide research and up-to-date information. The Internet is a valuable support in searching for help.

Notes for teachers

The OCR GCSE in Design and Technology: Textiles Technology allows candidates to acquire and apply knowledge, skills and understanding through:

- analysing and evaluating products and processes
- engaging in focused tasks to develop and demonstrate techniques
- engaging in strategies for developing ideas, planning and producing products
- considering how past and present design and technology, relevant to a 'design and make' context, affects society
- recognizing the moral, cultural and environmental issues inherent in design and technology.

Assessment objectives

Within this specification candidates will need to demonstrate their ability to:

- develop, plan and communicate ideas
- work with tools, equipment, materials and components to produce quality products
- evaluate processes and products
- understand materials and components
- understand systems and control.

The GCSE Subject Criteria (QCA 2000) sets out three specification assessment objectives for the scheme of assessment:

- AO1 Capability through acquiring and applying knowledge, skills and understanding of materials, components, processes, techniques and industrial practice.
- AO2 Capability through acquiring and applying knowledge, skills and understanding when designing and making products.

- AO3 Capability through acquiring and applying knowledge, skills and understanding when evaluating processes and products; and examining the wider effects of design and technology on society.

Examination

The terminal examination papers will test candidates' specialist knowledge, skills and understanding of Textiles Technology through questions on the subject content outlined in the specification.

Internal assessment (coursework)

The specification assesses QCA's three assessment objectives in an integrated way through the following six internal assessment objectives:

- identify a need or opportunity that leads to a design brief
- conduct research into the design brief which results in a specification
- generate possible ideas for a solution
- develop the product for manufacture
- plan and realize the product
- evaluate and test the product.

Websites

Examples of websites are suggested in the student book. Although these were up-to-date at the time of printing, it is essential for teachers to preview these sites before using them with students. This will ensure that the URL is still accurate and the content is suitable for your needs. We suggest that you bookmark useful sites and consider enabling pupils to access them through the school intranet.

DEVELOPING A DESIGN BRIEF AND DRAWING UP A SPECIFICATION

Developing and writing a design brief

Textile items are all around us in our clothing, furniture and transport. New textile products are always being developed, and some are totally new ideas. However, the majority are existing products redesigned to take account of current trends. Research into consumer needs often results in new designs.

A design idea is a solution to a problem. The problem is the starting point and must therefore be identified, for example, parents need a method of storing children's items in cars; solution: a fabric container attached to the back of the front seat. Solving problems like this meets people's needs.

Assessment objective 1: identifying a need/ opportunity leading to a design brief for a marketable product

If there is a practical problem to be solved, a design brief is needed. A **design brief** summarizes the aim of a design project and states briefly the kind of item that is needed. For example, consider the following problem:

> A major soft furnishing retailer wants to extend its range of bedroom furnishings to include the teenage market.

To come up with a design brief from this problem, think carefully about it and make a list of possible needs or opportunities. This will help you work out a design brief.

To satisfy the assessment criteria and gain up to 4 marks, you need to:

- **identify** bedroom soft furnishings, and research available products
- write a questionnaire to find out about teenage bedrooms
- use the questionnaire to survey a group of teenagers in order to find out what soft furnishings they like
- **analyse** the results of your research, in order to identify a need which leads to a design brief.

Writing a design brief

Identify bedroom soft furnishings

The first step in preparing a design brief is brainstorming. Brainstorm ideas for soft furnishings found in bedrooms. You might include items such as curtains, tie-backs, throws or lampshades.

Research available products

Research can be carried out in various ways. You could:

- visit soft furnishing retail outlets and make notes on bedroom soft furnishing products for teenagers
- look at magazines and mail order catalogues
- find Internet sites for bedroom soft furnishing ideas, e.g. Coloroll (www.coloroll.co.uk)
- word process or write up your findings.

Questionnaire

Write a quesionnaire to find out about teenagers' interests and the soft furnishing items that they would like in their bedrooms.

Questionnaire

I am a student at Holmesdale Technology College and I am required to design and make a marketable textiles product. Could you answer some questions about your bedroom and your interests? Thank you for your help.

1   Are you male/female?

2   Please give your age …

3   Do you have your own bedroom? yes/no

4   If no, is the person you share with older or younger?

5   How much time do you spend in your bedroom when you are not sleeping?
   - less than 1 hour per day?
   - 1–3 hours per day?
   - 4–5 hours per day?

6   How important is a comfortable and interesting bedroom? very/quite/not important

7   Do you have any of the following in your bedroom?
   TV/computer/CD player

Summary of results

A total of 25 people filled in the questionnaire.

1   **male or female**
   - male (8)
   - female (17)

2   **age**
   - 12–13 (5)
   - 14–15 (10)
   - 15–16 (10)

3   **own bedroom**
   - male (3)
   - female (15)

4   **sharing with older or younger children**
   - male (3 share with older)
   - male (2 share with younger)
   - female (2 share with older)

5   **time spent in bedroom**
   - 1–3 hours (8 males aged 12–16)
   - 3–4 hours (17 females aged 12–16)

6   **importance of comfort/interest**
   - 15 very/7 quite/3 not important

7   **items in bedroom**
   6 TV/20 computer/25 CD player

Survey teenagers about soft furnishing items

The results show that teenagers do spend time in their bedrooms and would like their bedrooms to be interesting. Now find out what soft furnishing items they would like by doing a further survey, asking which soft furnishing items they would like to see in their bedrooms.

Analyse results of research and identify need

You are already aware that teenagers would like their bedrooms to be comfortable and interesting; suppose that 15 teenagers said they would like to have a cushion and a lampshade as part of a co-ordinated room and 10 wanted curtains and bedspreads or duvet covers to match. A design brief can now be written to summarize the aims of the project as follows: 'Design and make a marketable soft furnishings product aimed at 12–16 year olds for use in their bedrooms'.

Activity

1   a   Write a design brief for the following problem: 'A high street fashion retailer wants to introduce a range of beachwear. Design and make a sample product'.

   b   Using Excel, key in the following information and chart the results.
   - sarong 17
   - bikini 12
   - swimming costume 10
   - T-shirt 9
   - hat 15.

Key points

- A design idea is a possible solution to a problem.
- A design brief summarizes the aim of a design project and states briefly the kind of item that is needed.

Examining the purpose of the product

It is useful at the beginning of assessment objective 2 (Drawing up a specification) to examine the intended purpose, form and function of the product in order to select appropriate **criteria** for the **design or performance specification**.

It is sometimes necessary to find out why and how a product was used in the past or is dealt with by different cultures, and to compare these findings with how the same product is used now. This process should provide a better insight into the needs of the user in relation to current trends within society.

It could be useful to break down the purpose into the subheadings:

- Who
- What
- Where
- How.

Beachwear project

Look at the student work on this page. It is evident that even though the form of swim and beachwear has changed dramatically, the consumer used the beachwear products for the same reasons in the nineteenth century as we do in the twenty-first, that is, for fashion purposes and as protection from the sun.

THE HISTORY OF BEACHWEAR

The purpose of this page is to show background information about three types of beachwear that I have collected.

BATHING SUIT

The late nineteenth century bathing suit was composed of two pieces: a long tunic and knickers which together almost completely covered the body. It was usually made of serge or wool and therefore unsuitable for bathing. Around the turn of the century this began to be replaced by one-piece garments. In the 1920's most bathing suits were designed for beachwear, rather than swimming. In the following decade backless costumes became popular. The invention of fast-drying and lightweight fabrics helped further to popularise swimwear. Swimsuits in the 1950's were often boned and corseted to emphasise the bust and minimize the waist. Briefer costumes began to appear during the 1960's, cut away around the tops of the thighs and around the arms and shoulder. This trend continued throughout the 1970's.

BIKINI

The bikini was launched simultaneously in France in 1946 by a little-known designer, Louis Réard, and a designer with a greater reputation, Jacques Heim. Early bikinis were trimmed and decorated with animal motifs and artificial flowers or were made of crochet. In the 1970's, a very brief version 'the string' appeared. Two minuscule triangles of fabric were held together by ties either at the hips or just one hip, and the bra-top was attached by ties around the neck and back, a design still seen today.

SARONG

The sarong is the traditional dress of the Malay Archipelago and the pacific islands where it is worn by both men and women. The sarong became popular in the 1940's for beach attire, a trend started by Dorothy Lamour, who wore sarongs in many of her films. Sarongs emerged again in the early 1950's when the basic wrapped and knotted shape was adapted for summer fashions.

SUMMARY - People wear beachwear to be kept cool and comfortable in summer. I must remember this for when I design and make beachwear.

WHAT NEXT? Research into theme: Aboriginal & Ethnics.

The history of beachwear – this information will make the selection of a specific type of garment easier, especially when targeting areas to cover for market research

THE PURPOSES OF MY PRODUCT

The purpose of this page is to find out what beachwear is used for now and to aid me to consider the qualities needed for the beachwear product. I will make fulfilling consumers needs so that my product will be a practical, marketable product.

WHAT is my product used for now?

⇒ On the beach – for sunbathing
　　　　　　　　– for swimming/paddling in the sea
　　　　　　　　– for beach sports ie. volleyball
⇒ In the swimming pool – for casual swimming
　　　　　　　　　　　– for fitness classes
　　　　　　　　　　　– for pool sports ie. water polo
⇒ By the pool – for sunbathing
　　　　　　　– for casual cool wear.

From the questionnaires issued to my target group I found that the most popular activity which beachwear is used for is swimming in the pool although all the other listed activities were things that beachwear is used for too, only they were not as popular.

WHAT are the purposes of my product?

⇒ To protect the body from the sun
⇒ To keep the person wearing it cool
⇒ To look good and be fashionable
⇒ To be comfortable
⇒ To absorb moisture
⇒ To be washable
⇒ To cover up parts of the body
⇒ To be waterproof so that it can be frequently used in water.

I asked my target group what they considered to be the main properties of beachwear apart from the fact that beachwear needs to cover up parts of the body and absorb moisture. The information I gathered was based around what my target group used beachwear for and so the information will give me an idea of the main properties needed for beachwear which will be used by my target group.

Graph to show what teenagers feel to be the most important qualities belonging to beachwear.

- ■ To protect body from sun
- □ To keep person cool
- □ To be waterproof
- ■ To be fashionable
- ■ To be comfortable
- ■ To be Washable

7%　16%
16%
　　　　　20%
22%
19%

My target group felt that the most important quality belonging to beachwear was that it should be fashionable and look good. I will definitely remember this point when designing and making my item of beachwear.

WHAT NEXT? The History of Beachwear.

The purpose of the product

I am looking at the reasons why children wear hats. This will enable me to know which requirements to meet, and what to include on my hat so that I finish with a product that will sell. It will help me make decisions as to fabrics, details and design, so that I can make a safe and practical hat that children will also think is fun to wear.

First and foremost my hat needs to be warm and hard wearing, because it is designed for winter. I must consider how much detail etc. to use, if it is going to survive outdoor play in bad weather conditions. I would think about using buttons, and other ways of fastening the hat to find a way of making it educational, so it could contribute to the child's learning. Another important factor is to make it seem fun for the child to wear, otherwise they will be constantly trying to pull it off their head, another reason why it needs to be durable enough to withstand tugging hands.

Why? - The purpose of a hat

Because their parents force them to. My hat should be appealing so that the child would enjoy, rather than hate, wearing it.

A winter hat must insulate the head, therefore the fabric should be warm, possibly waterproof, because 90% of the child's body heat is lost through the head. It should fit well to provide maximum warmth.

For educational purposes a child can learn to dress themselves, tie a bow with a hat fastening and learn how to use buttons etc. The hat could incorporate pictures of animals, along with their names? numbers? letters of the alphabet?

Why do children wear hats?

To protect the head the fabric must be hard wearing and durable. The hat cannot be too delicate, it must stand up to playing outside, and different weather conditions.

For fashion reasons. The hat may be part of a whole outfit. When making my hat, I could think about when and where it could be worn, eg with casual clothes, or for a smart occasion.

On the next page, I will consider different packaging and display methods associated with hats, in order to decide how I will package my hat and how best to present it to the customer.

The needs of the user – brainstorming a child's hat

The student has researched **what the product is used for** and **what the purposes of the product are** in society today. There are also references back to the questionnaire used in assessment objective 1 to reinforce the statements made. These results have been recorded on a graph, which has then been analysed with clear reasons as to the intended purpose of beachwear.

However, on this page it is evident that the student has had to research in more depth the needs of the user – as opposed to the historical aspect – in order to understand the purpose and need for a hat. For example, the developmental stages in a child's growth, as well as research into clothing needs and into the **performance characteristics** of a range of fabrics, are also needed. This student has also used a brainstorm effectively.

Activities

1 Choose a particular time period in history that interests you. How do you think current fashions have been influenced by this time period? Illustrate your answer.

2 Choose one specific product which has been influenced by your chosen time period. Is its function/purpose the same now as it was then? Give reasons why.

Key points

● A design will only be successful if it has a purpose and meets a particular need.

● It is important to consider existing products in both their past and present forms.

Identifying and evaluating existing products

5.1.1b, 5.1.2b, d, 5.2.4b

Once you have developed the design brief and considered the purpose of the product, the next step is to **identify** and **evaluate** existing products, taking into account the needs of the intended user.

Profiling

In evaluating the needs of the different consumer groups, it is useful to form a **profile** of each one, to help the manufacturer to identify the type of product a consumer will buy.

A profile of a consumer/market group would include:

- information about lifestyle
- the buying habits of the group
- age range
- gender
- where people live
- occupation.

Having produced a profile the manufacturer can produce ideas for a product to target a potential buyer. Profiling also helps in identifying a **niche** (gap) in the existing market that can be filled. In industrial terms, this is known as **niche marketing**. In profiling, other important factors are:

1 The **performance factor** of a product. For example, what does the consumer require from a product or the textile from which it is made? This factor can be measured by looking at the performance characteristics of the fabric – does it wash well? Will the product crease?

2 The **price factor** of a product. For example, what price will the consumer have to pay?

Market profile of my target group.

I have done this page so that I can get an idea of the size and shape of a certain group of children of both genders. I can also look at the shapes of their face and heads in general so that I can decide which hat shape will look the best on a child. The children pictured on my profile look to be between the ages of 6 months to 10 years old, they will not be expected to buy my product because they are too young. However, they will be an important group to target because they can often influence their parents choice.

Example of market profile

Ethnic cushions showing different blends and tones of colour and patterns

3 The **aesthetic factor** of a product. This involves personal taste and judgements, which change from one person to another. Because of this, manufacturers tend to generalize and are more concerned with how colours and shapes co-ordinate to produce a pleasing outcome for the user than with individual preferences.

4 The **cultural factor** of a product. This can relate to a **custom**, or an achievement of a particular consumer group, both in past and present society. For example, periods in history often influence present day fashion trends.

5 The **social factor** of a product. This involves the influence of different religions, beliefs and customs, places, pressures or desires on an individual within society.

Many fashion trends are started by pop stars

Marketing

Marketing is used to find out what demand there is for particular products and to work out how to encourage people to buy them.

When doing **market research** into existing products related to your own task, the five factors listed at left – performance, price, aesthetic, cultural and social – will help you to prioritize areas to focus upon and ask questions about:

● fabric types used to construct products

● popular themes, patterns or designs

● popular styles and types

● size range available

● range of alternative styles to suit a broad user need

● form of packaging and labelling

● form of display method

● price range

● environmental issues – reusable products.

Activities

1 Cut a picture showing a type of consumer group out of a magazine. Write a market profile for this group, using the notes on these pages to help you.

2 Suggest a range of textile products you could sell to this group. Annotate your ideas, showing the design features of each product and why you think it would appeal to your chosen group.

Key points

● A market profile for a product describes the type of people who buy the product.

● Marketing – the way in which a manufacturer or retailer promotes their products.

Organizing and planning market research

Allocating the right amount of time to this section of the design process can be difficult, so take care to plan your time carefully. Out of the 40-hour time allocation, full-course students need to plan on spending about 5–6 hours on the whole of assessment objective 2. Short-course students need to complete this section in approximately 3 hours.

Produce a rough plan of action, outlining all the focus areas of the market you wish to examine and evaluate. For example, what information do you need? What equipment/resources do you need? How much time can you allow?

Produce a list of the methods you could use to collect this information quickly and effectively. Here are some suggestions:

- interview consumers
- collect information from catalogues, magazines, leaflets, the Internet, TV
- visit retail outlets and exhibitions
- write letters to companies
- use questionnaires and surveys
- visit local textile manufacturers or find videos, CD-ROMs and books showing industrial processes
- take photos or use digital imagery

Presentation of market research

Once you have collated all of your information, it needs to be presented and justified. There are a variety of ways to do this:

- Produce a collage of all the types of existing products available on the market at the moment.

This could be composed entirely of a collection of pictures with notes outlining the current price ranges, colours, patterns, and types of product, styles and fabrics. (These notes could then be discussed in greater detail on subsequent pages.)

An example showing the collage method initially used to evaluate existing products

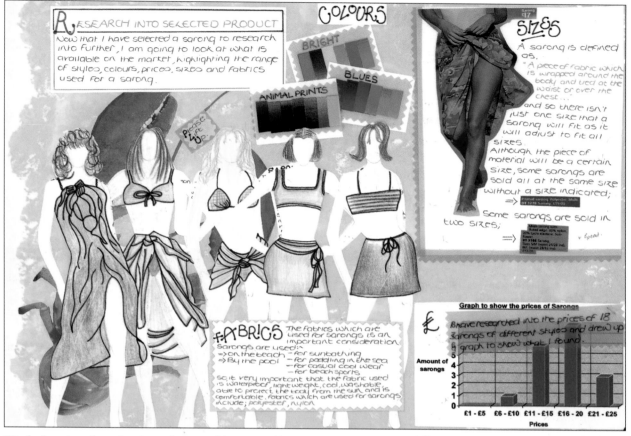

Work showing the selection of a suitable item of beachwear and an evaluation of existing colours, sizes and fabrics on the market

- Collate and analyse research using a database or spreadsheet and present it through the use of graphs, charts or diagrams, which can then be evaluated in more detail in relation to the needs of the user.

- Use text, mainly alongside sketches, photographs or clippings of existing products, with your personal views about user demands commented upon in detail.

At the end of your market research, you should have a clear idea as to what your target consumer group requires or needs from the product you are investigating and what type of product you will develop through your design ideas.

For example, if your task was to develop an item of beachwear, your market research should have identified a specific item for you to develop further.

Activities

1 Explain why market research is important in the development process of a new product.

2 How can market research be carried out?

Key points

- Market research is the gathering of information about products, by asking people's opinions and seeing what is available.

- Industry carries out careful market research before launching a new product.

- Market research should be relevant and effective.

Product planning and analysis

One of the best ways to help you to select a suitable item to make is to analyse and evaluate existing textile products on the market. This can be done by 'taking apart' an existing product to see how it has been made and what materials, components and construction techniques have been used. This process is known as **product analysis**. Look at the following example to find out how to evaluate and analyse a product successfully by asking yourself different questions.

Methods of construction:
- straight stitched flat seam used to sew around basic shape of glove, no seam finish on inside
- 2 main gingham fabric sections of glove, with polyester padded lining sections separate, stitched around edge to hold together
- bias binding used to neaten bottom edge
- care label sewn inside, swing tag outside

Functions:
to protect hand, wrist and lower arm when removing hot dishes from oven

Fibres/fabrics:
100% gingham for outer pieces
100% polyester for padded inner lining

Environmental issues:
cotton classed as natural fibre, biodegradable, could be recycled

Legal requirements:
manufactured to BS (British Standard) 6526 regulations

Performance characteristics:
- heat resistant
- durable
- easy to care for
- good insulator
- flexible
- lightweight

Size and ergonomics:
- made to fit adult
- extra room for movement
- anthropometric data (length 31cm, width 17cm)
- glove easy to control and flexible can be used on left or right hand

Trimmings:
bias binding to trim, neaten, finish bottom edge, also used for hanging glove

Colour scheme:
- green and gingham check
- other 'fresh' colours available

Questions to ask yourself in the analysis of an oven glove

- Does the product fulfil its intended purpose?
- What is the function of the product – how does it work?
- What method of construction has been used to make the oven glove? How is it stitched together? What type of seam is used?
- What colours are used in the oven glove? Is colour an important feature?
- Has the oven glove been **embellished**/decorated?
- How successful is this style of oven glove? What other styles are available?
- What is the cost of the product?
- What legal requirements does it need to meet?
- Is it **environmentally friendly**?
- What are the moral implications involved in producing the oven glove?
- Do the fabrics used have special properties or performance characteristics?
- What trimmings are used to make the oven glove? What is the purpose of this type of trimming?
- What type of fastening is used?
- What sizes are available?
- What fibres and fabrics are used to make the oven glove?

After taking the oven glove apart it is easier to answer the questions listed above.

Looking at the pieces

If you look at the pieces that make up the oven glove, you should now be able to make your own pattern using these pieces. If you understand how a product is made it is easier to suggest modifications and improvements to the design.

Product analysis in industry

In industry, in order to find out more about the competition, the product analysis of existing products is also the method used for product evaluation and research.

Trading standards

Trading standards officers check that manufacturers are meeting the legal requirements when making and packaging a product. They do this by taking a product apart. This type of checking is expensive because the item tested is usually totally destroyed by this process.

The Trades Description Act also makes sure that any claims made by the manufacturers about a product are true. For example, 'It is easy to wash at the specified temperature'.

Activities

1 What are the main benefits of evaluating existing products through product analysis?
2 Produce a chart or diagram to show how you could analyse and record information about an existing product relevant to your task.
3 Find out where your local trading standards office is situated. Write a report explaining how they can help to protect the consumer when purchasing a textile product.

Key points

- Product analysis means looking at a product in detail to find out more about it.
- By analysing existing products it is possible to find out how designers have successfully used existing materials and components.

Commercial production methods and systems

In deciding about a suitable textile product to design and eventually make, it is necessary to have a clear understanding of the different types of production methods and to have an insight into how industry caters for production in quantity.

What is a system?

Systems are used in industry to manage a process. A **process** is the way a product is made. The way a system is planned and designed can affect the standards of quality, efficiency and cost effectiveness. A system may make a task easier and more efficient. A system is made up of three parts:

Input	Process	Output
Manpower	Making of	Completed
Material	the product	product
Components		
Machines		

Industrial clothing manufacture

Industrial clothing manufacture is aimed at the mass market and is divided according to:

- target group – e.g. men, women or children
- type of garment – e.g. underwear, work wear
- type of material – e.g. knitted, woven

Industrial production of a textile garment is based on average consumer size. In women, this is size 14. Patterns and sizes are based on size charts and garments are produced in a limited range of sizes, e.g. UK sizes 6–20. 'Off-the-peg' manufacture is an example of this type of clothing manufacture.

'Off-the-peg' manufacture

'Off-the-peg' garments are cheaper because they are made to fit standard average sizes, not a particular individual. Alterations may be needed with off-the-peg garments before a perfect fit is achieved. One standard size template can be used for a production run and no fitting is necessary. This allows a batch of products to be made at one time, spreading costs over the whole batch and making the product less expensive.

Production systems

A production system is a way that a textile product may be made or produced. The type of production system used depends upon the product type, the amount or number of products to be made, the selling price of the products and the complexity of the design. The type of production system used can be individual or job production, mass or volume production, or batch production.

Individual or job production

This may also be referred to as '**one off**' **production**, jobbie, jobbing or making through. This is a traditional method of production where one operator or team assembles the whole of a textile product. Each product is a one-off, unique item, only made once in response to a brief or a specific client's request. This system:

- involves highly skilled operators
- involves high through-put time (time taken to complete products)
- is labour intensive
- uses versatile machinery (machinery that can be easily adapted to suit any textile process)
- operates with high levels of work in the system (which means that the work in progress is extensive and detailed).

Therefore, the end product is usually of high quality and cost.

Bespoke garments

Bespoke garments are individually tailored items, which are made to fit the exact shape of a person's body, and are an example of job production. Particular characteristics of a person can be considered in the cutting and sewing of such a garment, e.g. a rounded back. The customer selects the material and the design. This type of clothing production involves a much higher investment of time and cost. A single garment made to the specification requirements of a single customer is an example of bespoke clothing, e.g. the evening dresses made for celebrities attending the Oscars.

Mass or volume production

Mass or volume production involves large quantities of textile items being manufactured. It can be divided into two categories – repetitive flow production, or continual flow production. These two production methods are also known as **synchronized** or straight-line systems.

Repetitive flow production

This is also known as **flow line production** or unit production system. It relies on producing large numbers of identical products for a relatively low cost. The production of textile products is broken down into sub-assemblies of smaller **components**. While expensive to set up initially, the mass production of products leads to lower costs as:

- materials can be bought in bulk
- semi-skilled or unskilled labour can be used
- the initial high cost of machinery can be compensated for with a large output
- the system can be fully automated.

Continual flow production

This is the uninterrupted production of a textile product along an assembly line until it is complete. This method involves production for 24 hours a day to reduce costs because it is expensive to shut down.

Straight-line system

This system is suitable for producing large batches of textile products for large retailers. Work flows in a straight line through a series of assembly stations, each of which is synchronized to the next by ensuring that the time spent at each stage is the same. Each worker performs the same process over and over again on the identical part(s) of the textile product.

While there is a high turnover of textile products and a predictable production quantity, there is a high cost to change each production run and the process can frequently be disrupted through production difficulties and absenteeism.

Activity

1   Explain the advantages of off-the-peg garment manufacture.

Key point

● A well planned system in industry can guarantee a good quality product.

Batch production

Corporate identity

Batch production is used for larger, fixed quantities of identical textile products – either for stock (to retain by the manufacturer in case an order is placed for the item) or for order (an item made for a specific client or purpose, e.g. a T-shirt with company logo embroidered on the front).

Advantages

The advantages of this type of production method are:

- it is flexible and can be easily changed to meet the demands of the new orders coming in

- batches can be repeated as many times as needed with products being cheaper due to lower production costs

- a variety of styles can be made

- staff enjoy more flexible working conditions and receive training to ensure they are able to tackle each different batch.

Disadvantages

The disadvantages of this method are:

- lost time during the change in production of one textile product to another

- equipment needs to be re-set after each production run

- the increased number of textile products sometimes leads to the development of stock, which may cause storage problems and, if products remain unsold, wastage

- staff sometimes specialize in one aspect of production and work may therefore become repetitive and boring.

There are different types of batch production systems such as the **progressive bundle system** and the **section system**.

Progressive bundle system

The system of bundle assembly or the progressive bundle system means that workers are organized into sections according to the basic functions that make up a textile product, e.g. sleeves, pockets, small part and joining of seams.

The progressive bundle assembly system

The main advantages of a **progressive bundle system** are:

- smaller lot sizes

- delivery times reduced

- frequent product changes reduced

- can be combined with other systems, e.g. straight-line system (see p.19).

Section system

The section system, also known as **cell production**, may be used for producing batches of textile items. Unlike the progressive bundle system, the section system is used by factories that deal with frequent style changes and small numbers of items per product type.

Each worker specializes in a section of the assembly line constructing a garment component, which is then transferred to the next stage in the line. All sections are therefore situated close together. This type of system allows for easy product changes, but requires a lot of floor space and longer through-put time.

Commercial manufacturing systems

Just-in-time

Commercial manufacturing systems like **'just-in-time' production** help manage and control stock. This type of production requires regular deliveries of materials and components from suppliers, which arrive 'just in time' and are used immediately. This has advantages:

- costs are low due to reduced storage needs

- production is relatively fast

- quality is maintained during the making process and often improved

- materials and components are usually fault free (of the best quality) when delivered for final assembly of the product because goods are dispatched immediately to outlets.

Maintaining speed and quality during commercial manufacture is important.

In-line assembly

In-line assembly is where batch and flow systems are automated. Computers are programmed to ensure quality, while also offering versatility with mix and match facilities for some products to meet a customer's specific request, e.g. the addition of a company logo. This is known as **customizing**.

Safety

When mass producing textile items, some of the major considerations include the safety and well-being of the employees who are involved in making the products. Most companies operate a strict code of conduct to monitor this.

Your coursework

The information on pp.18–21 can be used in your coursework, using the methods highlighted in the examplar material on this page. You need to know how industry manufactures products in **batches**.

Assessment objective 2 –
Consideration of production methods

Job production

One product is made. The product is designed and made to specific requirements. The finished product is unique, e.g. 'designer hat'. Job production can be used for:
- making a prototype in response to a brief
- custom producing a specific product.

Products made in this way are often of high quality and take a long time to make. This can lead to a high cost product.

Batch production

Relatively small numbers of identical or similar items are made. Equipment and labour are then switched to another product, e.g. a hat (dress, children's, etc.) Batch production is cheaper than Job production because:
- materials can be purchased in bulk
- labour can be less skilled
- fixed production costs are spread over a large number of products

Problems could occur if the batch size is too large, leading to goods remaining unsold.

Mass production

Continual flow production

This is where products pass through a number of stages with each stage adding to the product. At each stage, machines or workers carry out a specialised task, e.g. cutters, stitching on the peak of the cap, stitching up the hat.

Repetitive flow production

This is where large numbers of identical products are produced as cheaply as possible flow production and is usually, used to make thousands or millions of products. This is called mass production. Although there is a high investment associated with buying the machinery to set up a production line, this system leads to lower unit costs. This is because:
1. materials are purchased in bulk
2. semi-skilled or unskilled labour can be used
3. production costs are spread over a large output.

This system relies on large and regular sales of products. The whole system is affected if there is a breakdown in the production line.

Summary

The retail outlet I've chosen is the national retailer Topshop. I've chosen mass production as everything is done using machines. The material is bought in bulk. This way, it is much cheaper for me to make my product. The target age to buy my completed garment is the same as people who shop at Topshop.

Purpose of page:
To look at the three different types of production

What's next?
Design specification

A student investigation into production methods

Activity

1 Write down a system for the production of an evening accessory – explain your choice in detail.

Key points

- Job production, batch production and mass production are all a type of production system.

- The organization of clothing manufacture ranges from small hand-made or bespoke operations to large industrial garment making.

Marketing and advertising in industry

Marketing

Once a textiles product has been designed and made it has to be sold. **Marketing** is the way in which a manufacturer or retailer promotes their products. Marketing, however, is more than just about selling. It involves finding out what people need, manufacturing commercially viable products, setting realistic prices, promoting products and selecting a suitable place to sell them. The main ways of marketing a product are research, advertising, packaging and display.

Research

Marketing begins with researching consumer needs. A company discovers a possible gap in the market and employs a market research company to investigate. It could be very expensive to manufacture goods in quantity without first researching the market. Surveys, questionnaires and interviews are some of the methods used. The market research company presents its findings to the client in a presentation which uses text, graphics and charts.

Advertising

Advertising is any type of media communication designed to inform and influence existing or potential customers. The cost of advertising is a major marketing expense, but essential if goods are to be sold at a profit. Initially, profits on new products are small, but if the market research company has successfully identified a product which meets a need and the advertising is successful, profits will be made. A company has to communicate with potential customers and promote their products.

Promotion concerns include raising customer awareness of the product; explaining the working capabilities of the product; explaining how the product will suit the customer's needs; and persuading customers to continue buying or to buy for a first time.

Many large companies employ advertising agencies to run their advertising campaigns. Products are advertised through the media to influence buying decisions, help sell more products and promote a good public image for the company. Media options include:

- magazines, newspapers (national, local, trade)
- TV, radio and cinema
- posters – billboards and transport
- directories – Thomson and Yellow Pages
- electronic – e-mail and the Internet.

Different media are used to attract different groups of consumers. A product aimed at men in their twenties will be advertised in magazines which appeal to men of that age group.

Images like this are used to advertise products to young men

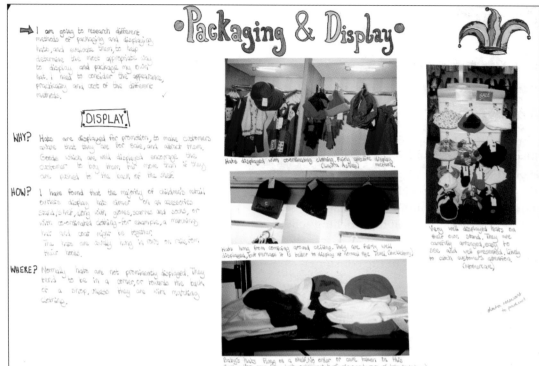

Student work showing research into the ways a hat can be displayed

All advertisements in the non-Advertising Standards Agency broadcast media (TV, radio and cinema) are controlled by the Advertising Standards Authority (ASA). The ASA ensures that advertisements comply with rules in the Code of Advertising Practice so advertisements do not mislead or make false claims.

Display

The quantity of textile products sold is influenced by the way they are displayed, for example, in shop windows, encouraging customers in. Inside the shop, items are grouped by design or colour. Clothing is displayed on mannequins with accessories to sell a whole outfit. Soft furnishings are displayed in room settings to sell more than one item.

A very exclusive way of displaying clothes is a fashion show. Models wear clothing from designers' new collections to show to the press, other designers and customers.

Catalogues are an important means of selling textile items. Some companies do not have a retail outlet and sell all their items by mail order direct to the customer.

Activities

1 Collect advertisements from magazines. What image is given by each product – luxury, middle range, or bottom end?

2 Promote your coursework product to consumers in your market group:
   a describe the features of your product
   b describe the lifestyle of your consumer
   c choose two different media for an advertising campaign and explain why each would be appropriate.

3 Visit two of your favourite clothing shops and evaluate their window displays.

Key points

- Marketing begins with researching needs.
- The quantity of textile products sold is influenced by the way they are displayed.
- Clothing is often displayed with accessories to sell a whole outfit.

Labelling of textile products

Labelling

Fibre content labelling is compulsory under the Textile Products (indications of fibre content) Regulations 1986. It initially came into effect in 1976, in accordance with EU (European Union) requirements for compulsory labelling of textile products. The purpose of the labelling scheme is to help:

- provide information to the consumer
- textile manufacturers in the EU by keeping both the names of fibres and the method of labelling throughout the EU the same
- with stock control in retail outlets.

The scheme applies to all new (unused) textiles sold to the public containing more than 80% textile fibres.

Fibre content

Fibre content may be shown on a textile product in a variety of ways:

- on a permanent label

- on a gummed label attached to the packaging

- on a ticket attached to the product (or roll of fabric).

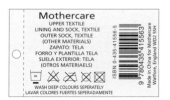

The retailer has the ultimate responsibility for making sure that the goods offered to the public are labelled.

Manufacturers and distributors are obliged to show the fibre content of goods passing through their hands.

If a textile product is made from a single unblended fibre type, it may be described by the use of its fibre name, e.g. '100% Cotton' or 'Pure Cotton' or 'All Cotton'.

PURE NEW WOOL

If a textile product in made up of more than one fibre, the two most important fibres must be named with the percentage (%) by weight of the fibre which each represents, followed by the names of the other fibres in order of proportion by weight.

Smart labelling

Advances in modern technology have led to more efficient systems in product labelling and identification.

In industry, the **Paxar 676** high resolution thermal printer has been developed by **Paxar UK** to print logos and care instructions in three colours on both sides of the label, without the use of the traditional labour-intensive printing plates.

Labels can be made out of a range of satin, coated and un-coated nylon and polyester fabrics, and can be produced as sew-on fabric labels, swing tickets and adhesive labels. Once printed the labels can be accurately cut and stacked by using **ultrasonic cutter and stacker units**, which read the printed label and cut it in the correct position. The advantage of ultrasonic cutting is that a smooth, softer edge is produced on the label, which reduces irritation for the user.

The advantage of the Paxar Printer System is that it offers the manufacturer a low-cost labelling system which is easy to use.

Hand held bar code scanners have also been developed with the facility to print and apply labels to products in one process.

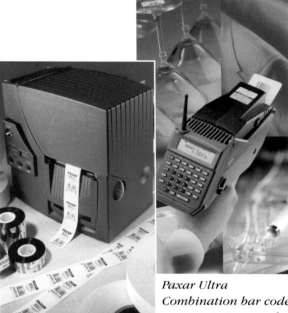

Paxar 9830Cl care label printer

Paxar Ultra Combination bar code scanner, printer and label applicator

Tagging

Radio frequency identification (RFID) tagging has been developed to enhance the existing bar code identification systems. The advantages of RFID tags is that:

- the information they store about a textile product can be changed or updated – a process which a traditional bar coding system cannot perform

- several items/products can be read or written together at any stage of the distribution process.

RFID tags can be checked manually with a hand-held terminal or electronically by use of an antenna.

How RFID tags work

These 'intelligent' tags are being used to identify specific items for specific manufacturing depots. They can be programmed with unique identifier, item ID, item description, time, date and status information prior to despatch to a store.
The whole process then becomes entirely automated – an antenna is used to read the tags as the garments arrive and the system automatically updates the store's computerized stock control system.

Checks can be made on the movement of the product within the store until the tag is removed at the point of sale or checkout.

The tag can be reprogrammed and reused to reduce production costs and provide a more environmentally friendly solution to tagging. In the future, durable tags might be built into selected textile products and contain Electronic Article Surveillance (EAS) theft-deterrence systems.

Intelligent tagging of a product

Activity

1 Produce a collage of care labels for different textile products. Choose one label and explain its meaning in detail.

Key points

- Fibre content labelling is compulsory by law in the EU.

- Tagging of textile products is used to help with effective stock control in retail outlets.

- Labels can be applied quickly and efficiently to give clothing manufacturers floor-ready garments that can be monitored at the store's exit and easily removed at the cash desk.

Packaging

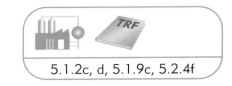

Packaging is needed for many reasons. Most importantly packaging is needed to:

- protect
- inform
- promote

Packaging is needed to protect the product. Customers need to examine the product before buying and handling could cause damage. Delicate designs/fabrics such as net need special protection. Products also need protection from being damaged in transit from the producer to retailer and from the retailer to the consumer's home.

Informing the consumer is another function of packaging. The consumer needs information about the textile product, e.g. fibre content, precautions, special treatments and washing/care of the item. The consumer must be told of flammability regulations and fibre content covered by the packaging (this is a legal requirement). The consumer can also learn of the company name, size of the product, age of the target group, the measurements and colour range, etc.

In promoting the product, packaging offers easy identification. The company and brand names are clear to the consumer, and can attract attention to the goods.

How do consumers react to packaging?

There are many ways a consumer may react to packaging:

- The consumer must have confidence that it will work and be fit for the purpose it is intended for.

- The packaging must suit the image of the product, e.g. if a textile product is of a 'standard or economy' range, the consumer will be disappointed with the contents if it is 'over-dressed' and may feel the product is over-priced.

- If a 'premium or high quality' product is 'under-dressed' by its packaging, the consumer may feel that it is too expensive.

It is important, therefore, that the quality of the packaging reflects the quality of the product.

The relationship between consumer and packaging is sometimes called **people** and **price points**. This means that the people for whom the product is intended will accept the cost of the item only if they think it is worth the price.

Environmental issues

Consumers can help to protect the environment by choosing to buy products produced in an environmentally friendly way, e.g. choosing to buy an unbleached cotton shirt. Manufacturers will then respond to consumer and government pressure to produce products that are less harmful to the environment.

With packaging, environmental groups state that the manufacturer, retailer and consumer should be able to reduce the amount of waste created. This can be done by:

- using reusable shopping bags
- reusing plastic carrier bags rather than taking a new bag in each shop
- not using extra unnecessary layers of packaging
- writing to manufacturers who have over-packaged their goods.

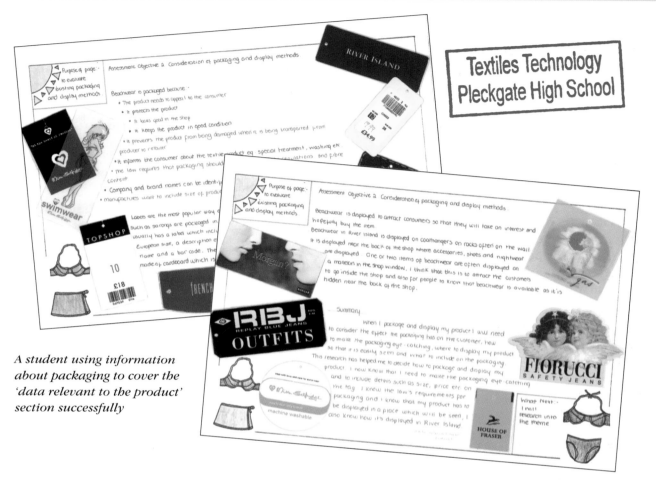

A student using information about packaging to cover the 'data relevant to the product' section successfully

Manufacturers will use recycled material to produce packaging if consumers choose to buy goods packaged in this way. However, until there is a big shift in consumer demand for recycled goods, manufacturers will continue to produce packaging using the most economic means which ensure that their products are not damaged between the production line and the consumer's point of use.

Considerations for packaging design

- What is the nature of the product to be packaged?
- Does the consumer need to see the product?
- Does the product need to be protected?
- Does the product need to be tried on or touched?
- Does the packaging need to be strong and functional, attractive, lightweight, flexible, easy to carry, etc?

Activities

1 Select a favourite piece of clothing you have recently bought.

   a Use diagrams to show how it was packaged.

   b Explain why you think it was packaged in this way and what the packaging tells you about the product.

Key points

- Packaging is used to inform the consumer, protect, sell and promote a textile product.

Developing a design specification

Having examined the purpose of the product, researched into and analysed existing products and other relevant information, the design specification can be developed. A specification of this type is useful to cross check against your design ideas and final proposal. These measures are taken to avoid making a product that does not meet your requirements.

A **design or performance specification** outlines how the product is expected to function and can include the following:

- **Time scale** of production – this includes your own deadline of 40 hours for full-course students and 20 hours for short-course students, in which to complete all coursework demands.

- **Function** of the product – what is the purpose of the product? For example, a child's hat should provide suitable protection during the winter or the summer depending upon the purpose as a sun protector or way to keep warm.

- **Performance** – how and where is the product meant to work? For example, a child's winter hat should be suitable for outside wear in the snow, rain or sun, should remain on the head, etc.

- **Aesthetics/appearance** – how will colour, line, shape, texture, pattern and form contribute to the visual appeal of your product?

- **Materials** – which materials would be suitable to use for the product? What performance characteristics are preferred for your particular product? For example, should the material be weatherproof, easy to clean, lightweight, biodegradable, etc.?

- **Manufacture/quantity** – how will the product eventually be commercially produced and in what quantities? For example, the hat should be suitable for batch production (approximately 50+ made) on an industrial basis.

- **Cost** – do you have to design to a budget? List the cost limits. The final cost should be within the range of £5.00–£10.00. (Use your market research results to guide your judgement for this section.)

- **Size** – are there any specific dimensions to be considered? Consider the overall shape required and the **tolerance range** of your measurements.

- **Target market** – which group of people are you designing your product for? What is their age, sex, interest, occupation, culture and religion? What image should this product create?

- **Ergonomics** – what effect should this product have on its human user? What information about the human body in terms of height, width, weight, reach, grip, angle of vision and range of movement will you need to use for this product? For example, the hat should be easy for the child to fasten and remove on and off the head.

- **Life in service** – how long will the product be expected to last? For example, the hat should withstand use for two or three seasons as the child is growing quickly and fashion trends change. A guarantee is sometimes expected with some products, e.g. sofas.

- **Weight** – does it matter if the product is light or heavy? Are there any specific weights to consider?

- **Safety** – what safety factors and regulations is it important to consider for the product?

- **Environmental issues** – are there any legal or environmental requirements the product should or ought to meet?

- **Quality** – how will you produce a marketable product? Consider **quality assurance** and **control** methods.

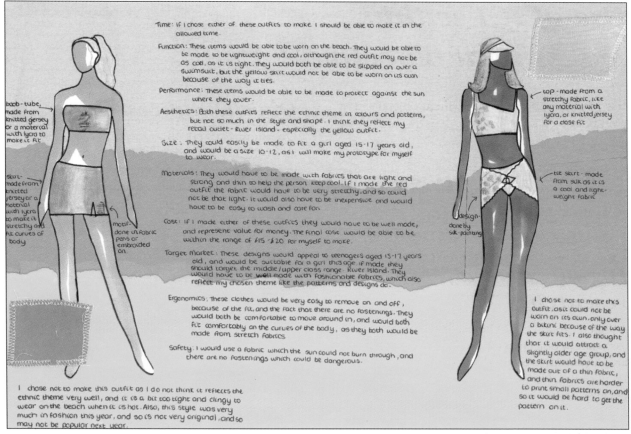

Time: If I chose either of these outfits to make I should be able to make it in the allowed time.

Function: These items would be able to be worn on the beach. They would be able to be made to be lightweight and cool, although the red outfit may not be as cool, as it is tight. They would both be able to be slipped on over a swimsuit, but the yellow skirt would not be able to be worn on its own because of the way it ties.

Performance: These items would be able to be made to protect against the sun where they cover.

Aesthetics: Both these outfits reflect the ethnic theme in colours and patterns, but not so much in the style and shape. I think they reflect my retail outlet - River Island - especially the yellow outfit.

Size: They could easily be made to fit a girl aged 15-17 years old, and would be a size 10-12, as I will make my prototype for myself to wear.

Materials: They would have to be made with fabrics that are light and strong and thin to help the person keep cool. If I made the red outfit the fabric would have to be very stretchy, and so could not be that light. It would also have to be inexpensive and would have to be easy to wash and care for.

Cost: If I made either of these outfits they would have to be well made, and represent value for money. The final cost would be able to be within the range of £15 - £20 for myself to make.

Target Market: These designs would appeal to teenagers aged 15-17 years old, and would be suitable for a girl this age. If made they should target the middle/upper class range. River Island. They would have to be well made with fashionable fabrics, which also reflect my chosen theme like the patterns and designs do.

Ergonomics: These clothes would be very easy to remove on and off, because of the fit, and the fact that there are no fastenings. They would both be comfortable to move around in, and would both fit comfortably on the curves of the body, as they both would be made from stretch fabrics.

Safety: I would use a fabric which the sun could not burn through, and there are no fastenings which could be dangerous.

boob-tube, made from knitted jersey or a material with lycra to make it fit

skirt - made from knitted jersey or a material with lycra to make it stretchy and fit curves of body

motif - done in fabric pens or embroidered on

I chose not to make this outfit as I do not think it reflects the ethnic theme very well, and it is a bit too tight and clingy to wear on the beach when it is hot. Also, this style was very much in fashion this year, and so is not very original, and so may not be popular next year.

top - made from a stretchy fabric, like any material with lycra, or knitted jersey for a close fit

tie skirt - made from silk as it is a cool and lightweight fabric

design - done by silk painting

I chose not to make this outfit, as it could not be worn on its own, only over a bikini because of the way the skirt fits. I also thought that it would attract a slightly older age group, and the skirt would have to be made out of a thin fabric, and thin fabrics are harder to print small patterns on, and so it would be hard to get the pattern on it.

An example by a short-course student showing the development of a design specification. Full- and short-course students are expected to produce the same depth of knowledge for a design specification.

These criteria should be used to produce guidelines to help you to develop your product further into the designing stage, helping you to evaluate initial designs which will lead to the final design proposal. This is evident in the example above.

The design specification should also help in the product development stage, investigating, trialling and testing suitable materials, production methods and pre-manufactured components, helping you to select and produce a quality, marketable product.

Use the specification points you have developed for your product to help you to determine your plan of action into assessment objective 3 and 4.

Activity

1 Select a textile product from a magazine or use one that is visible in your classroom. List the main criteria to be included in a design/performance specification for this product. Present this information in an imaginative way and include the use of ICT.

Key points

- A design or performance specification shows how the product is expected to function in use.
- A design or performance specification should be clear, detailed and always make reference to a control system for production in batches.

Use of ICT within assessment objective 2

5.1.8d, e, h

ICT can be used within assessment objective 2 in a number of ways:

- digital camera for research
- the Internet for research
- producing questionnaires for market research
- analysis of research
- word-processing, e.g. a design specification.

Digital camera for research

A digital camera could be useful in this assessment objective for recording how products are displayed, presented and labelled within a retail outlet. It is wise, however, to ask permission before using a camera in a retail outlet.

Displaying textile items

The Internet for research

The Internet is a useful source of information. Information about products is readily available and you can find appropriate sites within a search engine. Take a look at these two websites for a start:

www.british-shops.co.uk

www.matalan.co.uk

Questionnaires

Questionnaires are an essential part of this assessment objective, in order to target the user group. A word-processed questionnaire looks more professional and is likely to achieve a response.

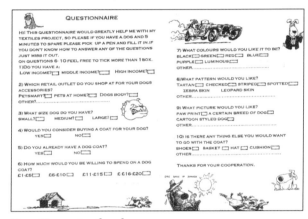

Questionnaire for dog owners

Analysis of research

Some of the research for this assessment objective requires analysis using spreadsheets and presentation through the use of charts. The charts can then be evaluated in more detail in relation to the needs of the user. Microsoft Excel or other spreadsheet packages can be used for this purpose and the evaluation can be word-processed.

Word-processing

The results of surveys and text alongside sketches, photographs or clippings of existing products can be word-processed using a word-processing package. Fonts can be changed to give a formal or more artistic slant to the research.

Letters to companies requesting information about products look more businesslike and are more likely to get a response if they are word-processed.

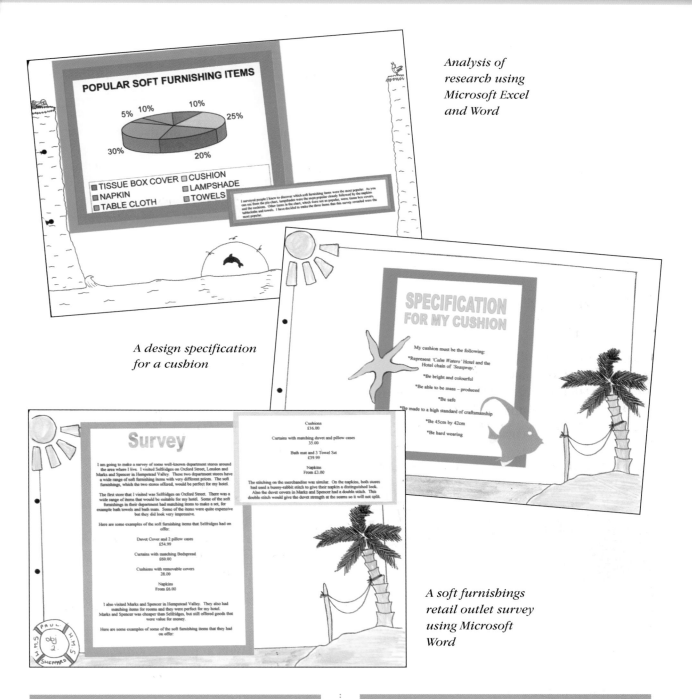

Analysis of research using Microsoft Excel and Word

A design specification for a cushion

A soft furnishings retail outlet survey using Microsoft Word

Activities

1 Word-process a letter to a retail company requesting information about a textiles product of your choice.

2 Devise a questionnaire using ICT for a textile sports product aimed at 14–16 year olds.

Key points

● Questionnaires and letters look more professional when they are word-processed.

● The majority of companies present their research using charts produced from spreadsheets.

Questions

1 List **three** pieces of information which could be included in the profile of a consumer or market group. [3]

2 A company is about to design a new type of school bag for primary school children. Write **three** questions that could be included in a market research questionnaire. [3]

3 A questionnaire is one way to gather information.

   a List **three** other ways which could be used. [3]

   b Explain **three** ways of presenting the information collected. [6]

4 Explain **two** advantages and **two** disadvantages of producing textile items using the 'progressive bundle system'. [4]

5 Explain the advantages of the 'just in time' production system. [4]

6 Which fibres are represented by the symbols shown below? [4]

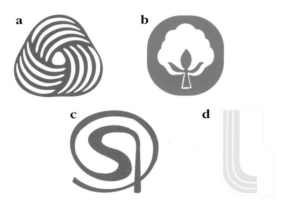

7 Information can be found on the label of a textile product.

   a State **two** pieces of information, other than fibre content, which could be found on the label. [2]

   b Explain why the information found on a label is useful to the consumer. [4]

8 Copy and complete the diagram below by identifying **three** other factors which could be included in the specification for packaging a pencil case. [3]

9 The illustration below shows a backpack intended for use by secondary school students. It is made out of denim fabric. Evaluate the suitability of the backpack for this use. Consider the needs of the users as well as the suitability of the design. [6]

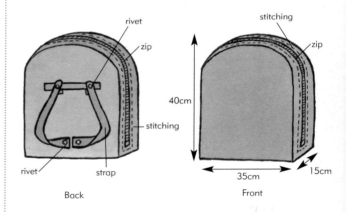

10 Brainstorm information that should be collected to help produce a specification for a case for a personal CD player. [5]

   Write a design specification for the case. [5]

GENERATING DESIGN PROPOSALS

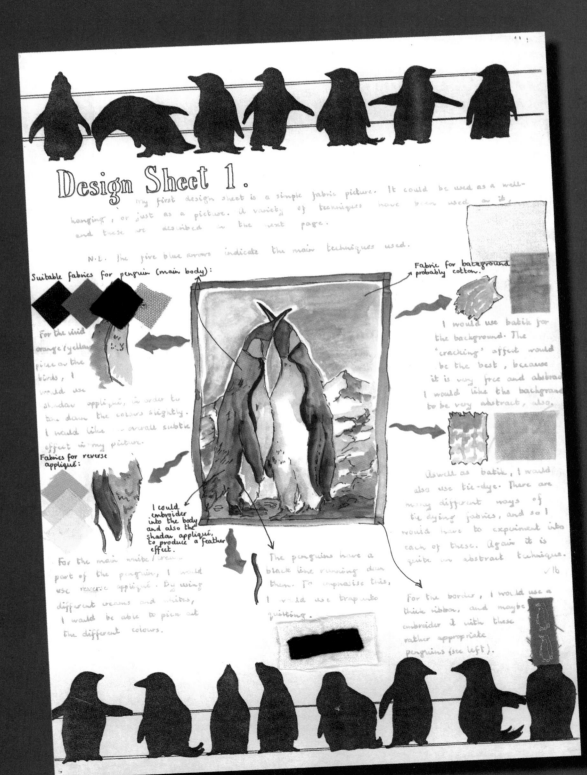

Generating design proposals 1

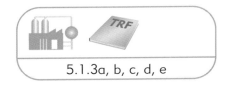
The design brief and specification give the information needed to begin the design process. Your coursework requires you to present your designs using a combination of text (written annotations/labels), graphics and ICT techniques including **CAD (Computer-aided design)**. It is important to understand the nature of design work. It can be done in a variety of ways using a range of presentation techniques.

Designing in industry

In industry, some designers specialize in designing one type of product or system whereas others are happy to design a range or collection of products. Designers may be employed full- or part-time or work on a freelance basis. A designer may produce totally new design ideas or may change existing designs to create interesting variations. A technique known as **attribute analysis** is often used for this process, where specification points are listed and customer needs considered. There are different stages in the design of a product before manufacture takes place.

Initial ideas

Initial ideas or **thumbnail sketches** are a mass of basic sketches done quickly. These can be worked on, discarded or developed further.

This type of sketching is useful to experiment with styles, shapes, patterns, etc. that are in your mind from previous market research ideas.

Thumbnail sketches designed by a full-course student to experiment with initial ideas

The mood or story board

In industry, designers will start with a collection of pictures, magazine articles, photographs and realia that can be put together in the form of a mood/story board or design notebook. This could include street scenes, man-made or natural shapes, colours, fabrics and patterns.

Designers use many things as a starting point for a design idea such as natural imagery, (for example a garden); paintings or works of art to reflect in a fabric print; or a musical trend, for example the 'come back' of platform shoes as worn by the Spice Girls.

Platforms worn by the Spice Girls

Role models such as pop stars or sports personalities can influence design, such as the popularity of the bandana or the sarong once worn by David Beckham.

Thumbnail sketches
These allow me to sketch out some of my preliminary ideas and to try out possible patterns and colour schemes. They helped me to collect my ideas together so that I knew where I was going and did not forget any of my ideas. They have narrowed down what designs I will go on to try as I can see from these/necessarily that some are not going to fit some of the points on my specification.

The mood board is an inspirational picture showing the starting point of the design idea

Industrial mood boards

An industrial mood board usually consists of four or five colours or tones used to complement or contrast with each other. Fabric swatches, trims, buttons, etc. can be added. Designers trawl catalogues from spinners and discuss qualities of yarns before developing their designs further.

Testing of new yarns and creating swatches in different structures gives the designer an idea of how the yarn feels, looks and handles. Once yarns are selected, key features can be developed on the selected design ideas: e.g. a pocket feature can be sketched, with construction techniques added. Paint charts from DIY stores can be helpful in choosing and displaying colour effects.

Developing your own mood board

When designing a mood or story board include the following:

- title or caption explaining the design theme
- photographs/magazine cuttings of the target consumer group using the product
- images to suggest the theme, e.g. drawings, wrapping paper, cards or realia
- fabric swatches, yarn samples, colour, pattern and technique details
- drawings of the product
- name of the designer/manufacturer and the season that the mood board is for.

Activities

1 Select an advert from a magazine as a starting point to produce a mood board for a textile product of your choice. Show clearly how your textile product has developed from the advertisement.

2 Explain how you could use ICT to enhance your mood board.

Key points

- The designer's function is to research, design and develop a product and to meet customers' needs.
- Most designers start working on products a year before they are sold.
- Thumbnail sketches are quick, freehand, basic sketches of ideas.

Generating design proposals 2

Working drawings

A textile product cannot just be produced from an initial drawing and a mood or story board – the design idea needs to be developed into a working drawing.

A working drawing shows a detailed outline of the textile product, the material to be used, the shape, size, possible trim details, fastening ideas, embellishment ideas and construction methods. Working drawings help the designer to sell his ideas to buyers from retail chains or directly to the consumer group.

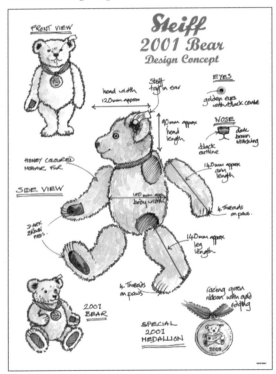

This working drawing of the Steiff 2001 bear has been used by the designer to directly target the consumer group

Working drawings are a useful way to show how design ideas meet the needs of the design specification. Clear and detailed **annotations** (labelling) are a useful method of showing this.

The examples shown here illustrate how full- and short-course students have successfully evaluated a range of design ideas against the main specification points.

Useful design tips

- Keep it simple at first – sketch simple, basic shapes.

- Try not to worry about being neat or accurate when brainstorming quick sketches.

- Select the best ideas and add more detail. Try photocopying the basic outline a few times first to generate quick, alternative detail.

- To make a fashion drawing from your design idea draw a body outline with exaggerated body and leg lengths or use a body stencil, and transfer your design to it.

- Create your own body stencils by tracing interesting body postures related to your theme, from catalogues or magazines.

- Collect fabric swatches, samples of yarns, threads and techniques, colour cards, pictures, textures, trims, etc. to create your mood board.

- Use a fine black pen to highlight important details.

- Create depth by using flesh-toned graphic pens/pencils to fill the body shape – remember to leave certain areas highlighted to give a 3D effect to your design.

- Use exploded drawing techniques (close-up views) to show in detail how the product is constructed.

- Avoid shading areas in felt-tip pen – use pencil crayons (preferably water-based).

- Always shade your designs in the same direction.

- Add detailed drawings of a specific area of interest on the product, for example, an enlarged view of a fastening or motif detail.

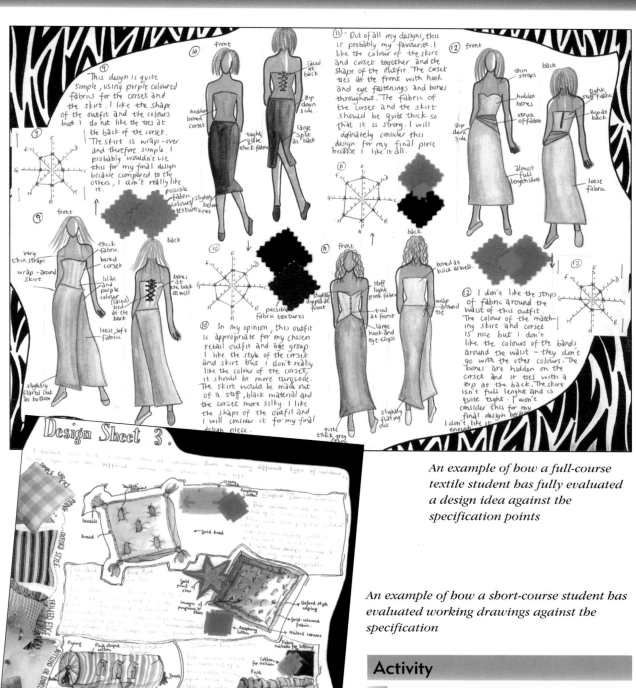

Design Sheet 3.

An example of how a full-course textile student has fully evaluated a design idea against the specification points

An example of how a short-course student has evaluated working drawings against the specification

Activity

1 Look at the textile product you have selected for your mood board. Produce a working drawing of this textile item.

Key point

- A working drawing is a detailed drawing of the design.

The final design

From the range of working drawings a final design proposal needs to be identified. The final design helps to produce the **manufacturing (product) specification**, so it needs to be fully annotated and evaluated, with reasons for selection clearly evident. This can be done in a variety of ways:

- clear annotations with additional notes made around the sketch examining construction details such as seam finishes, fastenings and possible assembly ideas

- the use of a chart or star profile to show visual evaluation of the design against the main specification points

- notes, which must be clear, precise and well written – do not cover any part of the design with text. Use arrows to link text with the design.

You must also remember that alongside the evaluation against your specification points you must clearly identify your final design choice with supporting evidence. Look at the example shown below. Factors which a designer must consider when preparing the final design idea are:

- current trends in fashion
- the competition
- colour trends
- cost or target price
- quality
- target/consumer groups
- retailer
- ease of industrial manufacture
- fibres
- existing ranges
- commercial viability.

Computer-aided design

Computer-aided design (CAD) helps in the rapid development of garment **prototypes** from initial sketches to finished garment. This is an important process because a potential buyer wants to see and feel a garment before they decide to produce it – the faster this stage can be finished the faster production can begin. This is especially important in the sports/leisurewear industry because of rapid changes in fashion.

In industry, some designers like to work directly on a computer; others find it easier to sketch by hand.

A final design idea fully explained against the specification and with clear reasons for selection

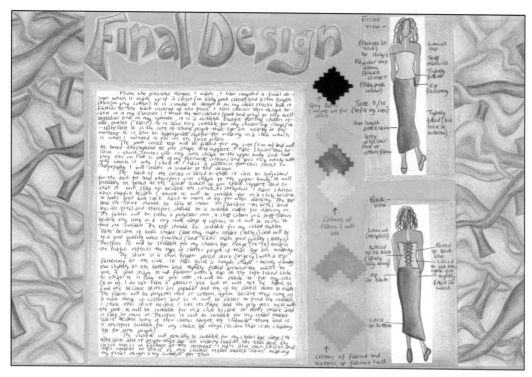

A detailed evaluation against the specification points covered in objective 2

CAD software is used to produce accurate drawings of the product and its components. Drawing a line at specific points generates a vector diagram; these points can then be moved to create the correct shape. The multiple selection of points allows the user to move them as a unit, retaining the relationship between the selected points. In the example below, the designer has used the Fittingly So package to manipulate and move lines in order to produce the main pattern pieces for a cloth bag.

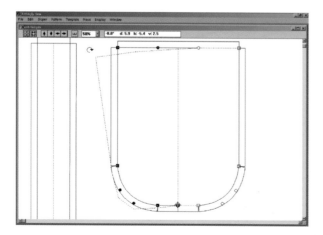

Fashion CAD allows designers to produce prototype garments and:

- produce 2D/3D drawings
- view all sides of the product, using the rotate facility
- enlarge parts of the drawing
- amend parts of the design on screen
- carry out tests and simulations.

Activities

1 Produce a final design idea from the working drawing you have completed.

2 Use at least one ICT technique to present your final design proposal.

Key points

- A final design is a completed, fully annotated and evaluated design idea.
- In industry, the final design idea is often used to help to produce the manufacturing/product specification.

Use of ICT/CAD to generate design ideas

It is important that you incorporate into your design work as many different techniques and materials as you can, especially through the use of ICT. The specification suggests that ICT be used where appropriate, even if it is just to produce text to enhance your presentation or to annotate your designs.

Use a scanner to scan in an outline template of the product. Flood fill the outline to create different colour and patterns, using a graphics program such as **Corel Draw**, **Paint**, **Draw** or **Publisher**. You could scan samples of fabric, threads and yarns directly onto the design page. It is relatively easy to import your own motifs, logos and pattern ideas (using a scanner) and to save as clip art images which you can reuse via a graphics program to develop further at a later stage. Use the scanner to create 'real-life' images onto fabric through the use of iron-on transfer paper. Try scanning sliced fruits placed on cling film on top of the scanner bed.

Graphics programs

Try using one of the many graphics programs for the designing of specific styles and care labels, for example, **Autosketch**, **Kidpix**, **Fads** and **Word** or **Paint**. Experiment with pattern tessellation to create pattern designs. Produce your own patterns, printing, patchwork or quilting ideas and save them.

When designing your mood/story board use scanned and digital imagery, sketches, text and realia to improve the final quality.

Texture mapping

Try texture mapping a garment or product design over a digital image to create different colour swatches – Paint and Draw programs are useful for this.

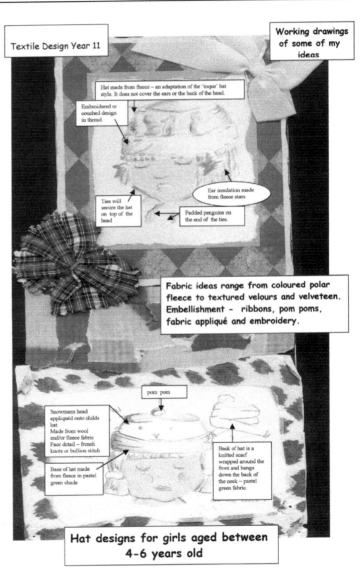

Use of scanner to create real-life images onto fabric

Word-processing

Annotate designs using a word-processing program with different font styles to express different themes. The example shown here has been annotated using Word, inserting text boxes over the scanned designs. The fabric and ribbon were scanned on the design and adjusted to the right position.

CD-ROMs

There are many CD-ROMs available both for providing textile design software and for information about the textiles industry. For example, you can create your own T-shirt designs using the Creativity range of software. Use these images to print onto transfer paper and iron onto the fabric. **Fittingly Sew** is also a useful package for designing.

ICTextiles

ICTextiles interactive design and manufacture software is available on CD. It gives tips on how to develop initial ideas to a successful product through the various stages used in industry. ICTextiles includes a rundown of the different kinds of design meetings looking at product range, merchandise analysis, machine capacity and niche markets. It also looks at other stages such as research, design, prototyping, assessment, marketing, production and retailing.

ICTextiles

Graphics tablet

The use of a graphics tablet to create or reproduce diagrams and drawings is useful and fun! A graphics tablet can:

- trace anything – pictures, drawings, photographs, body stencils, etc.
- allow you to draw freehand to achieve precision and accuracy
- allow you to create a symbol library to store patterns, shapes, etc., using AutoCAD
- allows you to move objects on the screen and select a range of commands, with a stylus (puck).

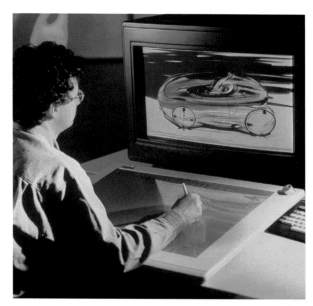

A graphics tablet

Activity

1 Produce a design proposal for a tie company. Scan and place on your design page a range of pre-manufactured components and fabrics which you will need to make your design.

Key point

- If used appropriately, ICT can be a useful tool to enhance design work.

Questions

1 List **four** possible starting points which a designer could use for inspiration. [4]

2 Explain what a mood board is and how it is used by a designer. [6]

3 Explain the meaning of the term 'thumbnail sketches'. [3]

4 List **four** pieces of information which would be included in a working drawing. [4]

5 The illustration below shows an initial idea for a school bag that could be used by a student to carry books to and from school.

   a Develop the design, taking into account the use of the bag and the intended users. Annotate your design. [4]

   b Explain the reasons for the modifications you have made to the bag. [4]

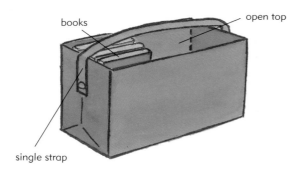

books   open top

single strap

6 Computer-aided design (CAD) is increasingly used in industry.

   a Describe **five** functions which can be carried out by a designer using CAD. [5]

   b Explain the benefits of using CAD. [5]

7 A new fast-food outlet is about to open in your area. The management has asked for ideas for the uniform to be worn by the employees. The specification for the uniform includes the following points:

- suitable for male and female staff
- suitable for all ages
- suitable for all figure types
- meet hygiene requirements
- be individual and distinctive
- be cost effective to produce and maintain.

   a Using the outline below, or an alternative figure if you prefer, sketch an idea for the uniform. Label the sketch to show **five** important design features. [5]

   b Explain how the design meets the specification. [5]

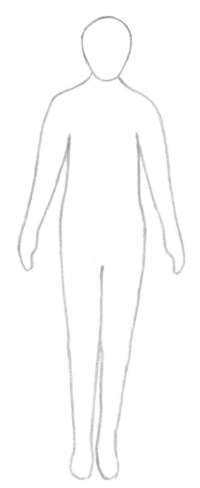

PRODUCT DEVELOPMENT

Fibres

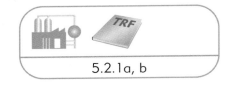
Natural fibres

Natural fibres come from plants and animals. *Cotton fibres* come from the cotton boll – the seed pod of the cotton plant. *Linen fibres* come from the stem of the flax plant. These are both cellulosic fibres. *Wool fibres* are animal hairs usually from sheep, but also from goats, camels, rabbits or llamas. *Silk fibres* are made by the silk worm. The worm uses the fibres to make a cocoon in which to change from a caterpillar into a moth. Wool and silk fibres are made from protein.

Man-made fibres

Man-made fibres do not occur naturally. One group of man-made fibres is known as *cellulosic fibres*. A natural starting point such as wood pulp is treated to extract the cellulose. This is then combined with chemicals to form a thick, sticky liquid like treacle. Next, it is forced through a spinneret to form long strands that are solidified using a chemical bath, warm air, or cold air. Fibres made in this way are *viscose*, *modal*, *acetate* and *triacetate*.

Fibres that are made entirely from chemicals are known as *synthetic fibres*. The chemicals used are generally from coal or oil. Fibres that belong to this group include *polyamide* (*nylon*), *polyester*, *acrylic* and *elastane*.

Recent developments

Microfibres are fibres that are less than one **denier** thick – very fine. They are lightweight yet strong, crease resistant, soft and drape beautifully. Polyester and nylon fibres are particularly suitable for this treatment. *Smart fibres* respond to changes in the environment in some way (see page 60).

The structure of fibres

The pictures below show the fibres as seen under a microscope.

Cotton fibres are shaped like a kidney bean or a figure of eight

Linen fibres are irregular in shape and have ridges like bamboo along the length of the fibre

Wool fibres are round or oval with scales along the length. Scales help with insulation, but cause problems when fibres are washed. They have a natural crimp

Silk fibres can be up to 3000 metres long. They are very smooth and have a rounded, triangular shape

Acetate fibres have ridges along their length, which differ depending on the type of spinning used to make them

Viscose fibres look very similar to acetate fibres and vary slightly depending on the type of spinning used to make them

Polyamide (nylon fibres) are usually smooth but the appearance varies depending on the spinneret

Polyester fibres are usually smooth, but the appearance varies depending on the spinneret

Performance characteristics of fibres

Every fibre has different performance characteristics or properties. It is useful to know what these are so that the best fibre can be chosen for a product, that is, the one with the most suitable performance characteristics. The table below summarizes the performance characteristics of the most frequently used fibres. The more asterisks the better.

Additional information

- Perspiration is a mild acid.
- Many washing powders are alkaline.
- Cotton and linen fibres are stronger when wet. Silk, acetate, acrylic and viscose are weaker when wet.
- Thermoplastic fibres can be heat set in place to make pleats.

- The durability of a fabric depends on its resistance to abrasion and its tensile strength.
- The way the fibre is made into a yarn, and the way the yarn is made into fabric, affects the performance characteristics of the finished fabric.

Activities

1 School jumpers are often made from acrylic fibres. With reference to their performance characteristics, explain why.

2 Summarize the performance characteristics of the following:
  a cotton fibres
  b polyester fibres.

Key point

- It is important to know the performance characteristics of fibres when choosing fabric for a product.

Performance characteristics	Acetate	Acrylic	Cotton	Linen	Polyamide (nylon)	Polyester	Silk	Triacetate	Viscose	Wool
Abrasion resistance	*	***	**	***	****	****	**	*	*	**
Absorbency	**	*	***	***	*	*	****	**	****	****
Crease resistance (stretch)	**	***	*	*	****	****	**	***	**	****
Flame resistance	*	*	*	*	**	**	****	*	*	****
Insulation	**	***	*	*	***	***	***	**	**	****
Moth resistance	****	****	****	****	****	****	**	****	****	*
Mildew resistance	****	****	*	*	****	****	*	****	*	*
Resistance to acids	***	****	**	**	*	****	*	**	**	***
Resistance to alkalis	*	***	****	***	***	****	*	***	***	**
Resistance to bleach	*	***	***	***	***	****	*	*	*	*
Resistance to build up of static electricity	*	*	****	****	*	*	****	*	****	****
Tensile strength	*	**	***	***	****	****	****	*	**	*
Thermal conductivity	*	*	***	****	*	*	*	*	**	*
Thermoplasticity	**	**	n/a	n/a	***	****	n/a	***	n/a	n/a

Blends and mixtures

Fabrics made from more than one type of fibre are known as a **blend** or a **mixture**. This combines the good performance characteristics of the fibres and reduces the effect of the less desirable ones. In some cases, the cost of the fabric produced is less than if one type of fibre was used.

A *blend* is when the fibres are mixed together before the yarn is spun. The different types of fibres are distributed evenly throughout the fabric.

A *mixture* is when one fibre is spun into a yarn for the warp threads, and a different fibre is spun to make the weft threads. The mixing occurs during the weaving process.

School or work shirts are often made from a polyester and cotton blend. The cotton fibres make the fabric more absorbent than if 100% polyester was used. This means that the garment is more comfortable to wear. The cotton fibres also make the fabric feel better.

The polyester fibres make the fabric more hard-wearing than if 100% cotton fibres were used. This is obviously very important for school and work shirts, which need to last a long time. The fabric is also easier to care for as it dries more quickly and needs less ironing, thus speeding up the washing process.

Shirts worn for work are often made from polyester and cotton blends

SAINSBURY'S LIFESTYLE	COLLAR
80% COTTON 20% POLYESTER	37 cm 14 ½ ins

Clothing label showing the fibre content

Another example is the use of nylon and wool fibres to make socks. Pure wool socks are likely to wear out at the heel where the shoe rubs it. The nylon fibres add strength to the sock. The wool fibres make the sock warm to wear and absorb sweat to ensure comfort.

A pair of wool blend socks

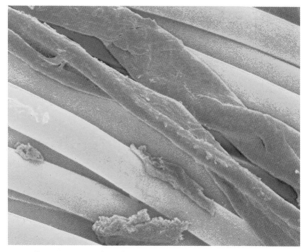

Dyed cotton and polycotton fabric

Combining a synthetic fibre with a natural one will allow pleats to be set into the fabric more easily than if a natural fibre alone is used. Using natural fibres with synthetics improves the comfort factor, and often the appearance of the fabric.

Cross dyeing

Different fibres take up dye to different degrees, a fact that can be used to create interesting effects in fabrics, but can also cause problems when colouring a fabric (see page 84).

A polycotton fabric which is dyed using a domestic dye will take up colour less well than a 100% cotton fabric, giving a paler result. This is because the polyester fibres do not absorb the dye as well as the cotton fibres.

If the fabric was a mixture rather than a blend, the cotton threads would take up the dye and change colour, but the polyester threads would remain unchanged. This would give a checked effect.

Activities

1 Look at the labels in the clothes you are wearing. Record the fibre content of each garment.

2 Use the information on the chart on page 45 to explain why the combination of fibres have been used in each case.

Bi-component fibres

These are made by combining two man-made fibres. The two liquids are forced through the spinneret at the same time and are joined before they solidify. There are three ways to join fibres.

- *Side-by-side bi-component fibres* are usually made from two slightly different polyamide (nylon) fibres, or two slightly different acrylic fibres. The fibre produced can be given a permanent crimp, improving warmth and bulk.

- *Core-and-sheath bi-component fibres* are made from two fibres, the one for the outer sheath needs to melt easily. These fibres are useful for making bonded fabrics (see page 59).

- Mixing the liquids together before they are forced through the spinneret makes *bi-constituent fibres*. This is an area for further development.

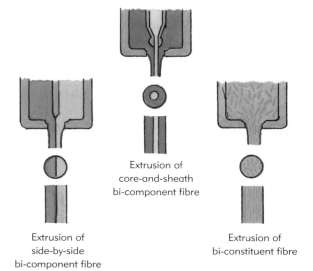

Extrusion of core-and-sheath bi-component fibre

Extrusion of side-by-side bi-component fibre

Extrusion of bi-constituent fibre

Key points

- Fabrics are often made from more than one type of fibre.

- The good qualities of the fibres are combined and the less desirable qualities reduced, improving the performance characteristics of the fabric produced.

Yarns

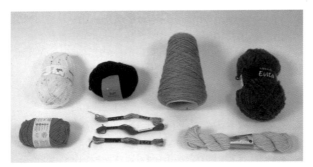

A selection of yarns

Yarns are made by twisting fibres together, a process known as **spinning**. The fibres are arranged to lie roughly parallel to each other and then they are twisted. The twist brings the fibres into contact with each other and the friction between the fibres holds them together. The exact process used to spin will change the appearance and performance characteristics of the yarn produced. The yarn can then be woven or knitted to make a fabric.

Cotton, linen and wool fibres are quite short and are known as *staple fibres*. A yarn made from this type of fibre has to be tightly twisted to hold the fibres together. This type of yarn usually has a slightly 'hairy' surface that does not reflect light well and so it has a matt appearance. It is known as a *staple yarn*.

Longer fibres are known as *continuous filament fibres* and need less twisting to form the yarn. The surface of the yarn is smoother and reflects light, giving a more lustrous appearance. Yarns made from continuous filament fibres are usually less bulky. This type of yarn is known as *filament yarn*.

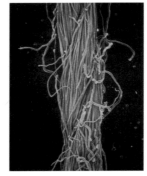

A staple yarn

'S' twist and 'Z' twist

When fibres are spun to make a yarn they can be twisted in a clockwise direction known as a 'Z' twist, or anticlockwise to produce an 'S' twist yarn. There is little difference in the qualities of the two yarns, but if two yarns are to be combined to make a more complex yarn, the direction of the twist becomes important.

The number of times the yarn is twisted in a metre is known as the *twist level*. Highly twisted yarns are smoother, thinner and stronger than yarns with a lower twist level. The tight twist squeezes out most of the air trapped between the fibres, reducing the insulation properties of the yarn.

Woollen and worsted spinning systems

The woollen system of spinning can be used to make yarn from almost any fibre, not just wool. In this system the fibres can be quite short and are not highly combed during the spinning process. This produces a yarn which is coarse and hairy. In the worsted system, longer fibres are used and they are repeatedly combed so that the fibres lie parallel. This gives a smooth, regular yarn which is hard-wearing.

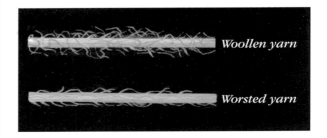

Woollen yarn

Worsted yarn

Complex and plied yarns

A yarn made by twisting fibres together is called a *single yarn*. This can be twisted together with other single yarns to form a *multiple-ply yarn*. Two single yarns twisted together make a *two-ply yarn*, three single yarns twisted together make a *three-ply yarn* and so on. As many as twelve yarns can be plied together. Plying yarns produces a stronger, more even yarn which is more balanced if a 'Z' twist is plied with an 'S' twist.

Multiple-ply yarns can be twisted together to make a *corded yarn*.

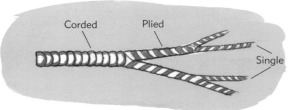

A corded yarn

This is a very strong yarn and has a wide range of uses from decorative embroidery threads to yachting rope.

Interesting effects can be created by twisting different colours and thicknesses of yarn together. Yarns made from different fibres can be plied together to combine the performance characteristics of the two fibres. Further effects can be achieved by the use of dyes on multi-fibre yarns, as the dye will be absorbed at different rates by the different fibres (see page 46).

All of these yarns are *plain yarns*, that is they are smooth and regular along their length.

Activities

1 Make a collection of different types of yarn and suggest uses for each.

2 Try knitting and weaving with a variety of plain and fancy yarns. Then, evaluate the results.

Fancy yarns

Unlike plain yarns, fancy yarns are uneven and vary along their length: they may be thicker in some places and thinner in others. They may also have knots or lumps at irregular intervals along their length. These yarns are often weaker than plain yarns, and can be more difficult to work with due to their uneven texture. Fabrics made from these types of yarns also have an uneven texture, and can develop holes if two sections of thin or weak fibre meet at a particular spot in the fabric.

 Snarl – *a very highly twisted yarn*

 Spiral *or* gimp – *a combination of a thick, soft yarn twisted with a fine, hard yarn*

 Boucle – *a wavy effect is created by feeding two different yarns into the machine at different speeds*

 Loop – *a stiffer yarn forms loops which stick out from a core yarn*

 Chenille – *a woven cut fabric yarn*

 Slub – *a yarn with thick and thin places*

 Knop – *a core yarn is held tightly while another yarn forms knops around it*

Key points

● A wide variety of yarns can be produced by varying the fibre used and the method of spinning.

● The fibre and spinning method affect the final performance characteristics and appearance of the yarn.

Weaving

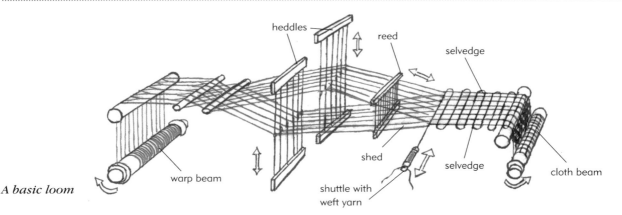

A basic loom

Weaving is the most common method of producing a fabric from yarn. Two sets of yarns are interlaced at right angles to each other on a machine called a *loom*.

One set of yarns is put on the loom. These are called the *warp* yarns. They have to be strong, in order to withstand the strain of the weaving process. They run the length of the fabric, which is known as the *straight grain*.

The *weft* yarns are woven in and out of the warp yarns, across the fabric. The weft yarns are carried across the fabric by means of a shuttle, a gripper, a jet of air or a jet of water.

The *heddle* lifts every other warp yarn to create a space known as a *shed*. The weft yarns can then travel across the fabric between the warp yarns. The first heddle is then lowered and the second one raised to create a new shed for the return of the shuttle.

The weft yarns are pushed into place by the *reed*.

Selvedges

When the shuttle reaches the edge of the fabric, it passes around the last warp yarn and travels back across the fabric. This means that the edge of the fabric does not fray. This edge is known as the **selvedge**. In some cases, the warp yarns are closer together at the edge of the fabric,

which makes the edge firmer. The straight grain of the fabric always runs parallel to the selvedge.

With some modern looms, a shuttle is not used and the edge of the fabric has a 'fluffy' appearance which makes it more difficult to identify as it resembles a cut edge.

Fabric widths

The width of a woven fabric is the distance from one selvedge to the other, following a weft yarn, at right angles to the warp yarns.

Fabric is generally available in a range of widths: 90 cm, 115 cm and 150 cm. Furnishing and upholstery fabrics can be wider than this. The width of the fabric is particularly important when calculating the amount of fabric required for an item. A commercial pattern gives the amount of fabric required for a range of widths.

Woven fabrics

Although there are an infinite number of variations possible, all woven fabrics have certain characteristics.

- Woven fabrics fray at cut edges.

- Woven fabrics are quite firm and do not stretch much. They stretch most diagonally across the fabric, known as the bias.

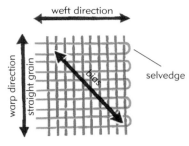

A woven fabric

- The fabric is strongest along the grain of the fabric, following the warp yarns.

- Two sets of yarns are visible in the fabric, one running up and down the fabric, the other running across.

Characteristics

The performance characteristics, appearance and cost of a woven fabric depend on a number of factors.

- The fibres used to make the yarn. The performance characteristics of the fibre greatly affect the finished fabric.

- The type and characteristics of the yarn used. For example, a textured yarn can be used for the warp, weft or both. This will give a textured fabric rather than a smooth one. Coloured yarns will create striped or checked patterns in the fabric.

- The thickness of the yarn used for the warp, weft or both. Ribbed effects can be created in this way.

- The spacing between yarns in the fabric. A close weave gives a strong, firm fabric which is more expensive to make than a loosely woven fabric. A loose weave fabric is weaker and pulls out of shape easily, but the air trapped between the yarns improves the insulation properties of the fabric.

- The order in which the warp and weft yarns cross each other. There are three basic weaves: *plain*, *twill* and *satin*. Each has different qualities and appearance.

- Special finishing treatments given to the fabric. These add particular qualities to the fabric (see p.90).

Examples of plain weave fabrics

Gingham – *a plain weave cotton fabric for shirts, used for blouses, tablecloths, etc.*

Organza – *a thin, transparent, slightly stiffened fabric, used for formal wear, interlinings, etc.*

Poplin – *slight ribs made using a fine, densely set warp and a coarser weft, used for furnishings, shirts, etc.*

Lawn – *a plain weave cotton fabric of high quality, used for many garments*

Shantung – *a plain weave fabric made from silk fibres, used for blouses, scarves, etc.*

Activities

1 Explain why such a wide variety of woven fabrics is available.

2 Find out the names and uses of some plain weave fabrics other than those listed above. Catalogues or the Internet are good starting points.

Key points

- Woven fabrics can be used for a wide range of products.

- Woven fabrics can be tailor-made for specific uses by careful choice of fibre, yarn and production methods.

Types of weave

The yarns used to make a woven fabric can be interlaced in a variety of patterns.

Plain weave

This is the simplest weave. The weft yarn passes over one warp and under the next. On the return, it passes over the yarns it went under on the previous row.

Facts about plain weave fabrics

- Plain weave looks the same on both sides.

- Its plain, even surface makes it a good weave to print on.

- As the yarns interlace with each other often, plain weave fabrics are likely to crease and do not drape as well as other weaves which use the same yarn.

- Depending on the fibre and yarn used, it can be a fairly hard-wearing weave.

- The thickness of the fabric produced will depend on the spacing of the yarns.

- The fabric can be thick or soft depending on the spacing between the yarns.

- This is the cheapest weave to produce.

Twill weave

This weave makes a pattern of diagonal lines or *wales*. The weft yarn passes over and under more than one warp yarn at a

time. In the following row, the pattern moves along one thread to create the diagonal characteristic of twill weaves.

Facts about twill weave fabrics

- Twill is the hardest-wearing weave.

- The front and back of the fabric look different.

- The surface of the fabric is uneven, so it will show the dirt less.

- The yarns interlace less often than in a plain weave. This means that the fabric is less likely to wrinkle. Also, the yarns can be packed closer together, making a firmer fabric. It is more likely to fray.

- More variations in the weaving pattern are possible with a twill weave than with a plain weave.

- This weave is usually more expensive to produce than plain weave.

Satin weave

In this weave, the weft yarns pass under between four and eight warp yarns before going over one. The right side of the fabric is smooth and shiny.

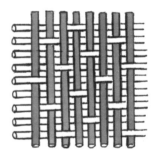

Facts about satin weave fabrics

- The warp yarns are set closer together and almost completely cover the weft yarns. This makes the fabric very smooth.

- The fabric frays easily as the yarns do not interlace very often.

- The warp yarns lie on the surface of the fabric and can snag easily. This means that the fabric is not very hard-wearing.

- The fabric will have a 'right' or 'best' side which should be on the outside of the product made from the fabric.

- If the yarns are set closely together, the fabric will be stronger, stiffer, more likely to wrinkle and more expensive than a loosely woven fabric.

Jacquard weaves

These weaves are very complicated. The Jacquard loom can be set to different sequences to produce intricate patterns within the fabric. Each warp thread can be lifted individually and the loom is often electronically controlled. The fabrics are very good quality and very expensive.

Pile fabrics

A pile fabric has threads or loops on the surface of the fabric. Velvet, corduroy and terry towelling are all classed as pile fabrics. In addition to the warp and weft yarns used to make the main fabric, called the *ground fabric*, an extra set of yarn is used to create the loop or threads on the surface. Loops can be cut as in the case of corduroy, or uncut as for terry towelling.

Corduroy is made by leaving extra threads on the surface of the fabric in lines. These are then cut to form the 'ridges' characteristic of the fabric.

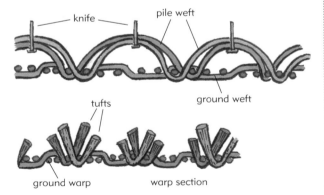

Velvet can be made in two ways. Two fabrics are woven face to face, with a set of yarns passing between them. The yarns are then cut to make two pieces of velvet.

Alternatively, yarns can be left on the surface of the fabric during weaving and then cut.

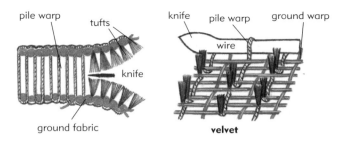

velvet

Facts about pile fabrics

- Pile fabrics are thicker and are therefore more hard-wearing than other fabrics.

- The surface is more ornamental.

- The loops on the surface of terry towelling increase the surface area, improving its ability to absorb moisture.

- The ground fabric (the threads which hold the pile in place) can be knitted or woven.

- Not all pile fabrics are knitted or woven. Some are made by 'tuffting', pushing little tufts of yarn or fibres into the backing fabric. This is a cheaper method.

- The quality of the fabric is determined by the density of the ground weave and the pile.

Activities

1 a Collect some samples of a range of woven fabrics. Using a hand lens, examine them to determine the weave used.

 b Suggest a use for each of the samples and justify your decision.

2 a Which weave would you recommend for a fabric to be used for:

 i a mechanic's overalls

 ii an evening dress?

 b Justify your choices.

Key points

- The performance characteristics of a fabric depend on the fibre or fibres used to make the yarn, the method used to make the yarn, and the way the yarn is made into fabric.

Knitting

The second most common method of making fabric from yarn is knitting. There are two types of knitting: *weft knitting* and *warp knitting*.

Weft knitting

Hand-knitted fabrics are weft knits. They are made from one long length of yarn. Loops are formed in the yarn which are interlocked with the rows above and below to form the fabric. Weft-knitted fabrics can also be made by machine.

Weft knitting

Facts about weft-knitted fabrics

- Weft knits are very stretchy, whichever fibre they are made from.

- The loop structure traps air, making them good insulators.

- Plain weft-knitted fabrics, known as single jersey, tend to curl at the edges, which makes them difficult to work with. Double jersey is made using two sets of needles and two sets of yarn, making a thicker, more stable fabric which lies flat but has less stretch.

- Weft-knitted fabrics are available in a variety of weights depending on the type of yarn used and the size of the loops. They can be made from natural or synthetic fibres, and a staple or filament yarn.

- A wide range of textures and properties can be created in weft knitting, as hundreds of different stitches can be used.

- Introducing coloured yarn can create a wide range of different patterns such as simple horizontal stripes, all-over patterns, pictures and single motifs.

- Weft knitting can create straight lengths of fabric or shaped fabrics ready to be sewn up to make a garment. Some weft knits are made as a tube, useful for items such as tights and socks where a seam would be uncomfortable.

- Circular knitting machines (see p.57) are popular in factories as they take up less room than a flat-bed machine and they are faster. This makes them economical.

- Computers can be used to control knitting machines, making it easy to set up and adapt to changing fashion.

- Weft knits ladder if a thread breaks, and when they are cut. This means that seams need to be stitched very securely to prevent this happening.

Uses of weft-knitted fabrics

Underwear, nightwear and baby clothing can be made from weft-knitted fabrics. The tubular construction of some knitted fabrics make them suitable for socks and tights. Pullovers, cardigans, hats and scarfs, which need to be good insulators, can be made from weft-knitted fabrics. Garments worn for sport and leisure, which need to stretch and move with the body, are often made from weft knits.

Jumpers are often made from weft-knitted fabrics

Swimsuits are often made from a warp-knitted fabrics

Warp knitting

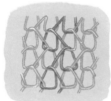

Warp knitting

In this type of fabric, loops are linked together from side to side. Warp-knitted fabrics are always made by machine.

Some facts about warp-knitted fabrics

- Warp-knitted fabrics can be firm, like a woven fabric, or stretchy. However, they are not as stretchy as weft knits and they keep their shape well.

- Warp-knitted fabric is usually made in flat sheets, not tubes.

- This is the fastest way to produce fabric.

- Setting up a warp-knitting machine takes a very long time. Each warp thread must be threaded individually, which for a wide fabric could take all day, making it an expensive process. This is the main reason why warp knitting is not used for 'fashion fabrics'.

- Most warp knits do not ladder, making them easier to cut out and sew together.

Uses of warp-knitted fabrics

Warp-knitted fabrics can be used for lingerie and foundation garments (e.g. corsets). Swimwear and sportswear are also often made from warp knits.

Lace, net and trimmings are frequently warp-knitted, as are fabrics used for curtains and bedclothes. Warp knits are also used for industrial textiles.

Activities

1 Make a collection of knitted fabrics. Examine them using a hand lens, to determine if they are a warp or a weft knit.

2 Suggest a use for each, giving reasons for your decision.

3 List the advantages and disadvantages to a textile manufacturer of making up garments from a weft-knitted fabric.

Key points

- Knitted fabrics can be recognized by loops in the structure of the fabric. They do not fray and they stretch more than a woven fabric.

- Weft knits have at least one yarn which runs across the fabric, forming loops. The loops are linked to the rows above and below.

- Weft knits are soft and supple, stretchy and crease resistant, but they do ladder.

- Warp knits are made by loops which run up and down the fabric, connecting from side to side.

- Warp fabrics are firm and stable, slightly less stretchy than weft knits, but still crease resistant. They do not ladder.

Knitting machines

Weaving is the main method of fabric production – knitting is the second most popular method of making textile products. For the classroom or small manufacturer, there is a range of knitting machines to choose from. These fall into three catagories:

1 *Plastic machines*. These are lightweight flat-bed machines which can knit a variety of different yarns. Patterns and designs are produced manually with the finished result being very similar to hand-knitting.

2 *Punch-card machines*. These are single or double flat-bed, metal machines that use plastic punch cards to create patterns and designs. They have a knitting carriage that slides across the bed of the machine and knits one row at a time.

3 *Electronic machines*. These machines use a pattern programming device instead of the traditional Mylar sheets and punch cards to create patterns and designs. The electronic machine has the facility to:

- scan pre-punched pattern cards and send the information to the machine bed where the needle positions are set

- enable the programming device to be connected to a standard TV set to allow you to design your own pattern ideas on a large screen. The cartridge from the device is then inserted into the knitting machine and transfers the design

- allow you to create and store designs from a PC using the disk drive connection. The disks can then be inserted into the knitting machine once the designs have been completed. Complete garment patterns can also be designed to full or halfscale using this feature

- produce a range of knitting techniques and finishes with a variety of special attachments.

In industry, flat-bed and circular weft machines are used for knitted textile products.

The **flat-bed machine** produces a continuous length of knitted fabric which can be cut and sewn together to produce items. Knitted products such as sweaters and cardigans are made in this way.

The **circular knitting machine** produces fabric in a tubular shape. This may be split along the length and opened up to make a full width of fabric. T-shirts, stockings and socks can be made using this method of knitting.

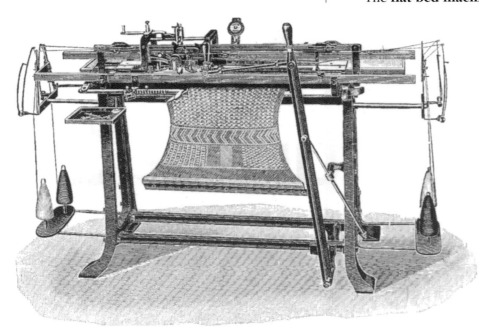

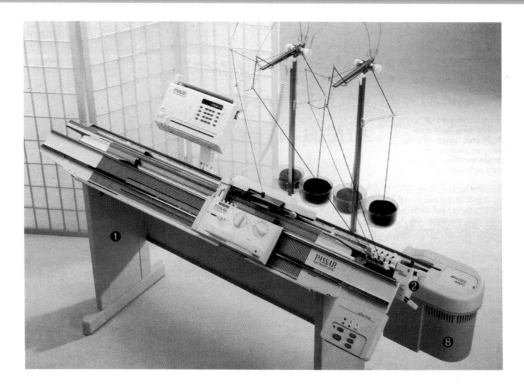

Advances over the century

While the basic function is the same, there have been significant advances in knitting machines in the last 100 years. At the turn of the century, machines such as the flat purl-bed machine:

- were expensive to produce
- were complex and therefore required specialist workers to maintain the machine and the knitting process
- were labour intensive
- meant production of knitted products was slow.

A hundred years on, the modern electric flat knitting machine has enabled the development of:

- controlled machining
- a reversible motor, programmable speeds and subsequently reduced time and labour intensive processes
- machine accessories such as the 'moveable Jack' on the needle bed which has led to more effective and efficient production of complex items

- programmable software and the simulation of fabrics and textile products on screen, increasing the speed of production and reducing labour costs.

Modern machinery has led to reduced waste and lower costs. However, it is not just better knitting machines that have led to higher quality knitted products. The quality of yarns has also improved.

Activities

1 Look at the knitting machines pictured on this and the opposite page – explain what factors have caused such rapid development of this type of machinery.

2 Draw a table to show the differences between warp-knitted fabrics and weft-knitted fabrics.

Key points

- There are two types of knitting – weft knitting and warp knitting.
- Warp knitting is an industrial process only.

Non-woven fabrics

Some fabrics are made directly from fibres without a yarn being made first. There are two groups of non-woven fabrics:

● felts

● bonded webs.

The first stage in making a non-woven fabric is to make a *web* of fibres, which can be done in a number of ways.

1 Air can be blown through the fibres so that they fall in a random arrangement; they are said to be *random laid*.

2 The fibres can be combed to lie straight, side by side, which is known as *parallel laid*, or two layers can be arranged at right angles, which is known as *cross laid*.

3 Man-made fibres can be pumped from the spinneret directly onto a conveyor belt, when it is said to be *spun bonded*.

The way in which the fibres are made into the web and the way the web is fixed together affect the performance characteristics of the fabric produced, including factors such as insulation, strength and elasticity.

Wool felts

Wool fibres have scales on their surface (see p.44) which can become tangled together, causing the fibres to stick to each other. This is the principle used to make wool felt. The web of wool fibres is treated with an alkaline solution and heated. Pressure and a mechanical action cause the fibres to become tangled together forming the fabric.

Facts about wool felts

● They are good insulators as air is trapped in the web.

● They can be moulded into shapes such as hats, and are soft.

● They can be made from recycled waste fibres.

● Felt fabrics are not as strong as woven fabrics.

● They do not fray.

Uses of wool felts

These fabrics are used for insulation materials, furnishings, roller coverings, hats, collar backs for jackets and coats, and billiard cloths.

Needle felts

Needle felt can be made from almost any fibre. A web is formed and then repeatedly punched with hot barbed needles. Fibres from the surface of the web are dragged through to the back to hold the web together. The web can be made stronger using one of the other methods of joining a web described opposite.

Wool felts are used for billiard tables

Facts about needle felts

- They are lightweight compared to most non-woven fabrics.
- They are generally more elastic than other non-woven.
- They do not fray.

Uses of needle felts

They are used for interlinings and waddings (see p.76), upholstery, floor coverings, mattress covers, coverings and filters. They are cheap to make and trap dust.

Bonded webs

The initial web for these fabrics can be made in the same way as non-woven fabrics. The fibres in the web can be bonded in a variety of ways:

- A binder or bonding agent (glue) can be applied to the web.
- A solvent can be applied which softens the surface of the fibres causing them to stick where they touch.
- If the fibres in the web are **thermoplastics**, they can be fused together by pressure and heat. This can be done in small areas at regular intervals, possibly using a hot needle.
- Special fibres which melt or dissolve to bond with other fibres can be included in the web.

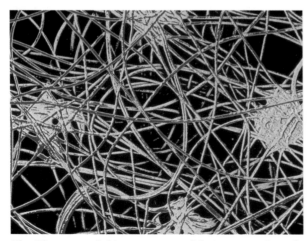

The filaments of this non-woven fabric are anchored by heat bonding (yellow patches)

Facts about bonded webs

- They do not fray, so can be cut using lasers.
- They are not as strong as woven or knitted fabrics.
- They do not stretch or give.
- They are permeable to air, that is, they let air pass through them.
- They have good crease resistance.
- As they usually have no grain they are economical to use. The pieces can be arranged on the fabric like a jigsaw, fitting closely together, saving fabric (see p.50 for straight grains and p.100 for pattern lays).

Uses of bonded webs

In garments, bonded webs are often used as interlining or interfacing. A fusible adhesive can be applied to one side which will melt at 120–180°C so that it can be attached to another fabric (see p.76). As bonded webs are relatively cheap to produce they are also used for disposable items such as cleaning cloths, tablecloths, napkins, underwear and hospital items. Bonded webs can be impregnated with chemicals, such as antiseptic for wound dressings and bandages.

Activities

1 Make a collection of non-woven fabrics. Examine them using a hand lens and determine how they have been made.
2 Suggest a use for each.
3 Investigate the uses of non-woven fabrics in industry. Start with catalogues.

Key points

- Non-woven fabrics can be made from almost any fibre.
- The way the web is formed and the method of fusing the web affects the performance characteristics of the fabric.
- Most non-wovens do not have a grain.
- They are economical to make and use.

Smart and modern materials

Fibre and fabric technological developments have produced a range of smart and modern textiles with many uses. It is important to have knowledge of what smart materials are and become aware of other smart and modern fabrics as they become available.

Smart materials

Smart materials can sense and react to environmental conditions and are produced to perform a particular function. There are three groups:

- **Passive smart**, which can only sense environmental conditions

- **Active smart**, which will sense and also react to environmental conditions

- **Very smart**, which can sense, react and adapt to environmental conditions.

The development of smart textiles has led to a wide range of new products being produced in the following areas:

- aerospace and transport

- telecommunications

- the home and other buildings

- clothing.

The product examples of smart textiles and fabrics include:

- smart skins for sound absorption and vibration control. These are mainly used in transport, e.g. planes.

- Fabrics which can create a sense of well-being through anti-stress or calm-inducing properties. Aristoc, for example, has developed a range of well-being tights impregnated with fragrant oils, moisturisers or vitamins.

- Wrinkle-free fabrics and garments.

- Heat-generating and strong fibres, for example fabric used for combat uniforms which change colour to fit the surroundings.

- Actively regulated micro-climate clothing to maintain temperature in extreme conditions.

- Clothing produced for radiation purposes.

- Garments or fibres designed to suit different conditions and hazard levels, for example Dupont have developed Personal Protective Equipment/Garments to reduce serious burns by switching from standard flammable polyester-cotton work-wear to a high performance garment system, based on Nomex fibres. The Nomex provides very high levels of heat and flame protection at low weights.

The flame resistance is part of the fibre's molecular structure, so the protective characteristics of the garment are enhanced and wear-life extended. Garments benefiting from this system include underwear, shirts, coveralls, single and multi-layer jackets, trousers, foul-weather wear, fleeces, gloves and facial protection.

- **Allergy control** fabrics encapsulated with substances needed by the body or with antiseptics.

- **Sanitized fabrics** for sportswear and socks, which contain microbial and anti-bacterial protection to combat sweat.

- **Fungal fabrics** used in clothing, linens, towels and carpets.

- **Synthetic fabrics** with moisture management properties which regulate and absorb sweat.

- **Intelligent polymer systems**, for example the smart bra which changes its properties in response to movement, giving better support

when needed. The bra will loosen the straps or stiffen and relax the cups in response to **polymer fabric sensors** which measure movement. It stores the information in a microchip and then signals the polymer fabric to expand and contract as needed.

Interactive textiles

An **interactive textile** involves the integration of a conducting network and a microchip into a fabric. The fabric is then capable of:

- computational operations

- conducting electricity

- collecting and storing energy.

Interactive textiles are used for gloves, caps and socks that are power-generated through movement, providing the wearer with heat, and for tents which will automatically become rigid in response to weather conditions and change shape to reduce wind loading.

Conductive and **fibre optic** threads woven into a garment with sensors and radio transmitters connected are being developed. Conductive polymers/fibres can be woven or knitted together with traditional fibres to produce a range of touch- and pressure-sensitive fabrics.

The performance characteristics of an interactive fabric include being lightweight, wearable, washable and durable as well as being cost-effective, simple, quick and desirable.

Activity

1 a Using the Internet as a resource, write a report looking at recent developments in 'fibres that protect'.

  b Illustrate your answer.

Key points

- All smart materials sense the environment.

- Some also react to the environment, and still others both react and respond to it.

Other fibres and fabrics

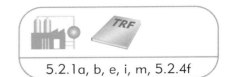
Elastanes

The best know elastane fibre is Lycra, made by Dupont. It is a filament fibre (see p.44) made from polyurethane. Elastane fibres can stretch up to eight times their original length and recover. They are fine, washable, resistant to light and can be dyed easily. Elastane fibres were originally used for items such as swimwear and underwear garments, but their use has expanded to include stockings and other stretch garments. They are also used for support bandages for sports injuries. Elastane fibres are often included in small amounts in garments which are not considered to be 'stretch' garments as the fibres improve comfort and appearance. They also reduce the need for ironing.

Leisure wear often contains elastane fibres

Elastane fibres are often used as a 'core' with a different fibre wrapped around the outside to give it a more natural feel.

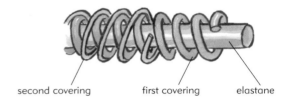

second covering   first covering   elastane

Polartec

This is a **biodegradable** polyester fabric made from recycled plastic bottles. It is warm to wear, lightweight and breathable. It has the same performance characteristics and uses as polyester fabric, but has the advantage of being recycled.

Breathable fabrics

Breathable fabrics are waterproof fabrics which allow perspiration to escape, making them comfortable to wear. The waterproof qualities come from the way the fabric is constructed. A barrier layer, often made from **microfibres**, is **laminated** to the outer fabric, or the lining of the product. This barrier layer can be coated with polyurethane to repel water. The fabric has pores which allow water vapour through, but are too small for droplets of water to pass through. The density of the fabric also traps a layer of air between the wearer and the garment to insulate against changes in temperatures. GorTex and Permatex are brand names of breathable fabrics.

Micro-encapsulation

Microfibres can be manufactured with a hollow centre. This can be filled with tiny crystals of chemicals or vitamins which are slowly released when the fabric is in use. The crystals are released slowly and can promote healing via dressings and bandages. The crystals last a long time and withstand wear and washing.

Nomex is used in garments for race car drivers because of its heat resistant properties

Kevlar

This material is five times stronger than steel but much lighter. It is used for bulletproof vests, flak jackets and other protective garments.

Nomex

This fibre has been developed for use in garments for firefighters, astronauts and racing car drivers. It has excellent heat resistant properties and can be mixed with a range of different fibres to make a variety of fabrics. It is also used for oven gloves.

Neoprene

This fabric is used to make wetsuits and other sportswear. It is a synthetic rubber combined with stretch fabrics and knitted fabrics. Warmth and softness are provided by the synthetic rubber which is environmentally friendly as it can be recycled.

Wetsuit made from neoprene

Sympatex

This is a very thin hydrophilic (water-loving) membrane made from polyester, usually included as an interlining between two layers of fabric. It is a breathable, waterproof fabric dense enough to act as a barrier to wind and water. These properties make it particularly suitable for adverse-weather wear.

Simpatex Healthcare, a manufacturer of scooter and wheelchair weatherwear, has introduced a product which provides comfort and insulation. This is done by having a waterproof nylon outer fabric, a lightweight **Thinsulate** microfibre inner layer for warmth and a soft polyester fleece lining for comfort. Reflective material is also used to improve visibility.

Activities

1 Use the Internet to research recent developments in fibres and fabrics. Trade magazines will also cover this topic.
2 Compile a scrapbook of the information.

Key points

● New fibres and fabrics are constantly being developed. The Internet is essential for keeping up to date with new developments.

● They are usually made to meet a need.

Testing and trialling fabrics

When the final design proposal has been decided, the next stage of the process is to develop the product. An important initial step in this is to test and trial the design proposal. This is in order to:

- make decisions about what materials, **pre-manufactured standard components** and production processes to use

- match materials and components with suitable tools, equipment and processes.

The quality of the product depends on the initial specification. Within this, the main aim of testing and trialling is to improve the quality of the product for the user. The next few pages look at testing materials.

Testing materials

There are many types of tests that can be carried out on materials to find out how they perform. When testing the **performance characteristics** of materials you can test:

- tensile strength
- durability in relation to wear and tear or colour
- **abrasion** (wear) in relation to **pilling**
- absorbency
- insulation
- flammability
- waterproofness
- windproofness
- fading
- **drape**
- aftercare – washing, ironing and stain removal.

Testing in industry

In industry, rigorous testing ensures that materials conform to the strict standards that are set for high quality.

Tests that may be carried out in industry include:

- testing yarns to see how much abrasion (wear) they will take before breaking

- testing the durability of fabrics in relation to wear and tear. The Martindale abrasion machine may be used to do this.

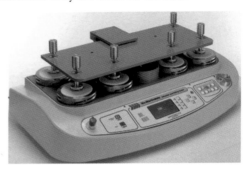

The Martindale abrasion machine is used in industry to test a fabric's wear and tear

Brainstorming

It is useful to begin by thinking about what types of testing and trialling could be done for a specific design proposal. These initial ideas could be presented as a spider diagram, mind map or brainstorm.

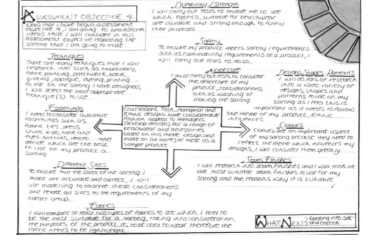

A student's initial brainstorm for developing a range of beachwear based on ethnic designs

Testing for wear and tear

Testing for wear resistance

A simple classroom method to test wear resistance (abrasion) of a fabric is to rub two blocks of wood together – one which has been covered with sandpaper and the other with strips of different types of fabric. To carry out this test you should:

1 Rub the two blocks in the same direction with an even pressure.

2 Either count the number of rubs until a hole is formed in the fabric or rub for a set amount of time (e.g. 5 minutes).

3 Compare the results for the different fabrics.

This test can be further developed by stretching two pieces of the same fabric onto a board. One piece should be wet, the other dry. Then:

1 Rub the two pieces of fabric repeatedly with a pumice stone, a coin or a piece of sandpaper on a block.

2 Note whether the wet or dry fabric shows signs of wear first, and whether the colour is lost before the fabric begins to wear.

Recording the results

Results of testing and trialling should be carefully logged using a table, chart or star profile. The diagrams on this page show how a student has successfully tested and evaluated a range of fabrics for wear resistance.

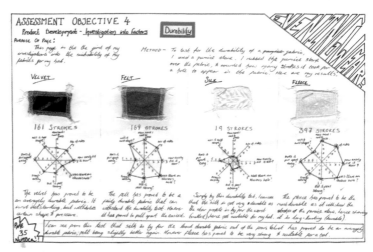

Recording the results of an abrasion test

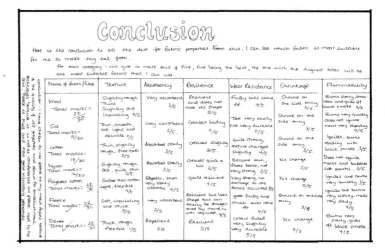

Comparing the properties of different types of fabric

Activities

1 Carry out your own abrasion tests on a natural, man-made and synthetic fabric.

2 What conclusions can be drawn from the results? Give reasons for your answer.

Key points

● All testing and trialling must be appropriate to the design proposal.

● Comparative testing is important to achieve a quality, marketable product.

Testing flammability

Fire-testing of textiles looks at their burning behaviour and the risk involved in their use. Different fabrics and materials burn at different rates, therefore knowing how a fabric behaves when it is set alight is important, especially when designing and making a product for a child or an item of soft furnishing. The test outlined below shows a good way to find out how flammable a fabric is.

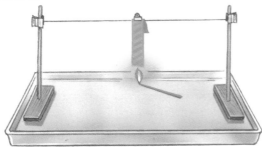

Testing to see what happens to a fabric when burnt is extremely dangerous. It is therefore important that you are supervised during this test

1 Cut pieces of fabric 3 cm. wide into lengths of no more than 20 cm. Attach each strip of fabric (one at a time) to a wire line, as shown in the diagram above.

2 Set each piece of fabric alight using a splint and record the following:

   ● colour of flame

   ● speed of ignition

   ● smell

   ● type and quantity of smoke

   ● nature of residue.

In industry, the most common method used for testing fire resistance is watching the spread of the flame on a product.

   The fabrics used in industry may be treated for **flame retardance** to meet British Standard specifications. These treatments fall into four catagories:

1 Non-substantive finishes are usually water-soluble products that give off gases which swamp the oxygen supply and stop flames forming.

2 Substantive finishes, the most common type of treatment, and used on textiles which have to be regularly laundered or dry cleaned, e.g. Proban and Pyrovatex.

3 Reflective surface coatings are added to enhance thermal properties as well as making the product more resistant to fire.

4 Back coating, which is done by spreading the reverse of a fabric with a mixture of fire-resisting chemicals and resins, which are then allowed to dry. This is a popular treatment for carpets and floor coverings.

Labelling

Common labels found on textile products to show that they have been tested for fire resistant properties are shown in this picture.

Flammability labels

Testing absorbency

Some fabrics and materials absorb water and other liquids easily. This is due to the type of weave and/or the actual fibre. There are two simple ways to test how absorbent a fabric is.

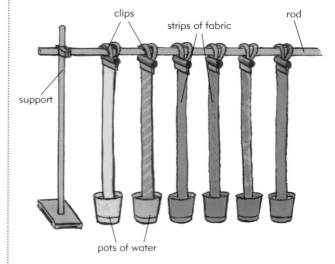

Testing fabrics for absorbancy – method 1

Method 1

1 Cut strips of the same width and length in different fabrics. Secure the strips along the length of a supported rod.

2 Place a pot of cold water under each strip so that the fabric dips into the water.

3 Record how quickly the water is absorbed by the fabric.

Method 2

1 Weigh each fabric sample to be tested in a container you already know the weight of and calculate the dry mass of the samples.

2 Dip each fabric strip into cold water for 20 minutes; weight them down, otherwise the fabric strips are likely to float.

3 Remove the excess water from each piece of fabric by shaking it 10 times at one-second intervals. To find out how much water has been absorbed, weigh the fabric strips again.

4 Subtract the dry mass of each sample from its **wet mass**: this will tell you how much water has been absorbed by each piece.

Testing for stretch

It is important to test the strength and stretch of a fabric when designing and making textile products like soft furnishings or items for supporting loads, e.g. bags. It is important that the fabric used has good **recovery** properties and does not increase in length or sag.

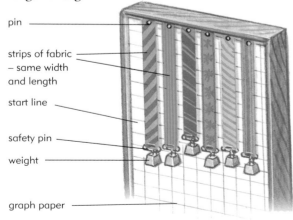

pin

strips of fabric – same width and length

start line

safety pin

weight

graph paper

Testing fabrics for stretch

Testing for stretch and recovery

You can test this by setting up a frame from which you suspend the fabric samples.

1 Cut fabric strips of the same length and width. Pin a large sheet of graph paper to a wooden board and draw a level line across the top of the paper; pin each fabric strip along this line.

2 Draw another line along the bottom edge of the fabric strips. Stand the board upright and attach equal weights to the bottom of each strip. If you have no weights, stretch and pin the bottom of each strip to the board. Leave for one hour.

3 Mark the new position of each fabric strip.

4 Remove the weights or pins and leave the fabric for 10 minutes.

5 Mark the final position of each fabric strip.

This will show you how far each piece of fabric stretches. If the fabric has a long stretch and recovers to its original length, once the weight is removed it has good elasticity.

Activities

1 What fabrics would you choose to make a child's nightgown? Explain why.

2 How would you label this product to explain how flammable the fabric is? Illustrate your answer.

3 Give a detailed explanation as to why some textile items would benefit from being made out of a stretch fabric. Find pictures to illustrate your answer.

Key points

● Tests must be performed fairly.

● By performing these tests, you will better understand how a fabric's properties can suit the purpose of a product.

Testing to see if a fabric is water-repellent

It is possible to test for waterproofness by seeing how resistant a fabric is to water spray. A simple classroom method to test this is as follows.

1 Stretch a sample of fabric over an embroidery hoop and hold it upright.

2 Using a spray nozzle, direct 250 ml. of water onto the fabric.

3 When the spray has stopped, turn the fabric upside down and tap firmly, twice, to remove excess water.

4 Use the diagrams below to help you show the rate of absorbency for each fabric sample; the circle labelled 1 is the most waterproof; 5 is the least waterproof.

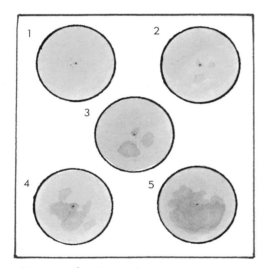

Degrees of water resistance

In industry, testing a fabric's water repellency can be done using the Shirley Hydrostatic Spray Rating test. This measures the pressure needed to push water through a fabric.

Testing air permeability

Testing the air permeability of a fabric is a measure of how windproof it is. This is important if you are designing and making products which need to keep cold air out.

The Shirley Hydrostatic Spray Rating tester is used in industry to test if a fabric is water-repellent

A simple classroom test is as follows:

1 Cut pieces of fabrics to be tested to an equal size (approximately 15cm. square).

2 Hold one of the pieces of fabric in front of a mirror and blow gently for 1 minute; watch carefully to see if the mirror mists over from the heat of your breath.

3 Repeat this process for each of the pieces of fabric.

4 Write down what happens.

Simple classroom test for air permeability

Testing insulation

This is an important test if you are designing and making a textile item which needs to keep the user warm and prevent too rapid a heat loss, e.g. a child's winter hat. To test whether a fabric is a good insulator the method described below can be used.

1 Collect either identical plastic bottles with screw-cap lids or test tubes, as shown in the diagram above. You will need one for each fabric tested and one for the control.

2 Cut fabric samples of the same size to completely cover the bottle or test tube around the sides.

3 Wrap each bottle or test tube with a piece of fabric and secure with elastic bands. Leave the control uncovered.

4 Pour an equal amount of hot water (not boiling) into each bottle or test tube.

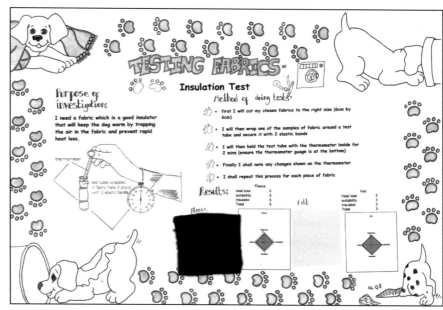

An example by a full-course student testing insulation properties of a fabric

Measure the temperature of each one quickly. Replace the screw cap if you are using bottles.

5 Leave for a specified time, e.g. 10 minutes, then measure the temperature of each bottle or test tube again, including the control.

6 Carefully record the results by plotting the temperature loss against time on a graph, to show how good each fabric is as an insulator.

The higher the second temperature reading, the better the insulation properties of the fabric.

Activity

1 Make a list of all the textile products you can think of where an insulation test should be performed. Illustrate your answer with pictures from magazines, brochures, etc.

Key points

● Ensure that the fabric size is the same for all samples for each test.

● A fabric is a good insulator if it prevents rapid heat loss.

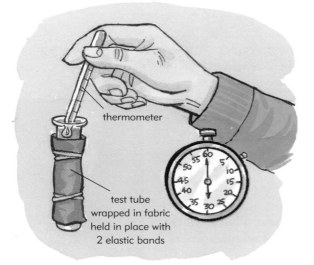

thermometer

test tube wrapped in fabric held in place with 2 elastic bands

Simple method to test the insulation properties of a fabric

Testing for fabric care

Stain resistance

Depending upon the product you are making, you may need it to be stain resistant – a washable fabric will clean and dry better. The illustration below shows a simple test for stain resistance.

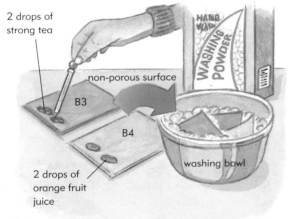

2 drops of strong tea

non-porous surface

B3

B4

2 drops of orange fruit juice

washing bowl

Stain resistance test

1   Cut pieces of fabric to be tested to the same size. Use a pipette to put a drop of the stain required on each piece of fabric apart from a control piece, which will not be washed.

Suggestions for stains using a pipette:

● strong tea

● oil

● orange juice, e.g. on children's wear
Alternatively rub the required stain onto the fabric.

Suggestions for stains to be rubbed:

● grass, e.g. on sportswear

● chocolate, e.g. on children's toys/clothes

● lipstick, e.g. on evening wear

● suntan lotion, e.g. on beachwear

In each case, note whether the stain stays on the surface of the fabric or is absorbed quickly.

2   Wash each sample in hot soapy water, rinse and leave to dry. When the samples are dry, check to see if the stain remains on the fabric (use the control piece to help you compare the samples).

3   Record your results using a scale of 1 to 5, where a clear visible stain scores 1 and a clean piece of fabric scores 5.

Colour fastness

A simple test to check this can be done in the following way.

1   Cut two fabric pieces, approximately 10 cm. square for each fabric type to be tested. One piece will be tested, the other will be the control piece.

2   Machine stitch the fabric pieces to be tested together to form a long strip. Do the same with the control pieces.

3   Machine wash the strip to be tested on a high temperature wash. When the fabric is dry, compare it with the control strip to see if there is any colour fading. Repeat the test for five, ten or more washes.

These samples can also be tested for shrinkage when compared with the control pieces.

Testing suitability for ironing

A lot more 'smart' fabrics and finishes are being produced which do not require ironing after washing, termed easy iron/non-iron fabrics.

60% COTTON
40% POLYESTER

NON – IRON SHIRT

NEXT

Product label showing non-iron logo

However, it is useful to test the effect of direct heat on a fabric, especially when using a synthetic fabric or a fabric with a pile. To test this:

1 Cut four fabric pieces, (5 cm square) for each fabric type to be tested. Place each piece of fabric on a strip of foil which, when folded in half, will cover the fabric piece completely.

2 Place one of the foil parcels (with the fabric in the centre) on an ironing board. Iron with a pre-heated iron on a cool setting for one minute.

3 Repeat this process using the rest of the samples with a pre-heated iron on a medium setting and a hot setting.

4 Remove the fabric samples from the foil and record carefully what has happened. Look for colour loss/fading, shrinkage or melting, singeing or discolouring, flattening of surface texture/pile, extra lustre or shine to fabric surface.

5 Present your results (use symbols from page 73).

Washability

Some of the textile products you make will need to be washed. It is important that they still look good after frequent washing. To test this:

1 Cut four pieces of each fabric to be tested to the same size, approximately 5 cm square.

2 Wash one piece of fabric at 40°C, one at 65°C, and one at 90°C. One fabric piece should be kept unwashed as a control.

3 Leave to dry.

4 Repeat this process and note your findings.

5 Use a chart to record the results. Comment on colour change, shrinkage, creasing and pilling. Use a mark out of 5 for each aspect and add up the final score. Which fabric looks the best after a few washes?

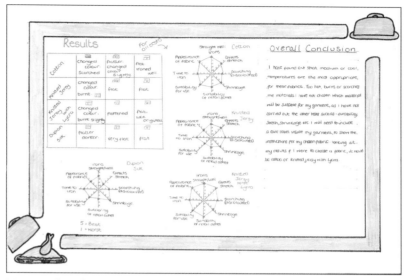

Test results after washing

This test is useful to help create a care label for the product.

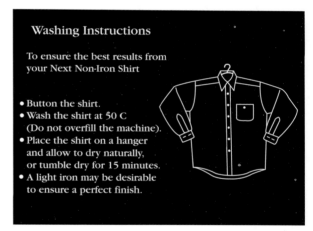

Washing Instructions

To ensure the best results from your Next Non-Iron Shirt

- Button the shirt.
- Wash the shirt at 50 C (Do not overfill the machine).
- Place the shirt on a hanger and allow to dry naturally, or tumble dry for 15 minutes.
- A light iron may be desirable to ensure a perfect finish.

Care label for a shirt

Activity

1 Make a list of products which need little or no ironing. Explain why in detail, with reference to their fibre properties.

Key point

● New technology and manufacturing techniques have changed the traditional laundering care of textile products.

Care labelling

Care labelling

In assessment objective 4 you are required to devise a care label for your completed product. Use the information in this section to help you to create an accurate label.

Care of fabrics

All fabrics collect grease and absorb dust through wear and handling over time. If fabrics are to last they require cleaning in the form of washing or dry cleaning. It is important that the products are cleaned without damaging the fabric, because textile items are often expensive and the correct care will keep them in good condition for a greater length of time. All manufactured textile items have a label showing the fibre content as well as a care label to tell the user how to keep the product in good condition by using the correct method of cleaning.

Modern textile fibres are made from a wide variety of fibres, so they need to be laundered in different ways. It needs to be clear on the label what the **aftercare** instructions are to ensure that the textile product is not ruined when cleaned.

Washing process

When fabrics are washed, they should be washed at a temperature to suit the fabric. Detergent is used to dissolve dirt and stains. Mechanical action (agitation to loosen dirt from the fibres) and rinsing with clean water complete the washing process. After washing, the water is removed by wringing or spin drying. The item is then dried, either by hanging on a clothes line or by tumble drying. Once the item is dry, ironing at a temperature suited to the fabric may be necessary to remove any excess creases.

The new Dyson washing machine has two drums

Aftercare instructions

Aftercare instructions and labelling are chosen according to the type of fibre used in the product and its performance characteristics. The strength of the fibre, sensitivity to chemicals and temperature, and mechanical action are important performance characteristics in this context. Fabric construction such as loose weaves or special finishing processes can also limit washing methods. Laundering tests are carried out on fabrics to determine correct care labelling (see p.70).

Symbols

Textile items may be made in one country, but sold in many others. In order that everyone understands how to care for textile items, a set of symbols – the International Care Labelling Code (ITCLC) – has been developed.

These symbols are used in most European countries and throughout much of the world. The care code is based on five basic symbols and a cross.

Symbol	Meaning
⊔	Machine or hand Wash
△	Chlorine Bleaching
⌒	Ironing
○	Dry Cleaning
▢	Tumble Drying
✕	DO NOT ...

The washtub symbol is used either on its own, or with a bar or broken bar symbol:

Symbol	Meaning	Process
⊔	Cotton Wash	Normal wash action and spin
⊔	Synthetic Wash	Reduced wash action and reduced spin
⊔	Wool Wash	Low wash action and slow spin
⊠	No Wash	Unsuitable for washing
⊔	Hand Wash	Unsuitable for machine washing

The wash symbol may also contain further details for the best possible wash:

Symbol	Suitability	Description
95	White Cotton and linen without special finishes	Wash as Cotton
60	Cotton Linen Viscose colour fast at 60°C	Wash as Cotton
50	Nylon, polyester/cotton, cotton/acrylic mixtures	Wash as Synthetics
40	Cotton Linen Viscose colour fast at 40°C	Wash as Cotton
40	Acrylics, Acetate and wool/synthetic mixtures	Wash as Synthetics

The ironing symbol shows which temperature to use for a given fabric:

Symbol	Temp	Suitability	Description
⌒	200°	Cotton, Linen, Vicose	Hot Iron
⌒	150°	Polyester mixes and wool	Warm Iron
⌒	100°	Acrylic, Nylon, Acetate, Polyester	Cool Iron
⌒̸		This symbol is used to indicate that ironing will damage the garment, **not** that it is Easy Care	Do Not Iron

The tumble dry symbol shows whether the garment is suitable for tumble drying and which heat setting should be used:

Symbol	Meaning	Description
⊙⊙	Tumble dry at high heat	Tumble drying is possible
⊙	Tumble dry at low heat	Tumble drying is possible
⊠	Do Not Tumble dry	Do Not Tumble dry

The dry cleaning symbol is important because it informs the dry cleaner about which dry cleaning solvent to use:

(A) All solvents

(P) Perchloroethylene

(F) Certain solvents only

Activity

1 Using the information in this section, devise a care label for:
- white cotton shirt
- woollen jumper
- your chosen coursework product.

Key points

- Modern textile items are made from a variety of different fibres and need to be cleaned in a number of different ways.
- The care labelling code has been developed so that everyone knows how to care for individual textile items.

Textile components 1

Pre-manufactured standard components are items that are used in addition to fabric, for example:

- *thread* – to join fabric pieces together and for topstitching
- *fastenings* – to allow textile items to be fastened and unfastened repeatedly
- *linings and interfacings* – for support, insulation, pockets, waistbands and added shape in textile items
- *decorative components* – used to decorate textile items, e.g. beads, fringing, zips
- *functional or structural components* – used to give shape or fit to a textile item, e.g. shoulder pads, bondaweb, boning, elastic and bias binding

Thread

The strength of a textile item is greatly influenced by the type of thread used to join the pieces together. A quality sewing thread will have the following performance characteristics: strength, elasticity, resistance to detergents and sunlight, and availability in a range of colours and shades. There are different thread ranges for hand and machine sewing. The thread used must match the fabric in both fibre and weight.

Most modern threads are made from polyester which has all the performance characteristics required (strong, elastic, resistant to detergents and sunlight, available in a range of colours, does not shrink). Cotton thread is still used because of its strength and versatility, although it is more expensive than polyester. Viscose thread is mainly produced for embroidery because it can be produced with a lustre, takes dyes extremely well and is inexpensive.

Linen and silk threads are available for specialized items. For example, in **haute couture**, a designer may choose these for silk and linen items because their performance characteristics will match the item and they can be dyed to give an exact colour match.

Fastenings

Choice of fastening is governed by the function and design of the item. Some need to be functional rather than decorative and some need to be invisible. When choosing a fastening, the following factors should be considered:

- Who will be using the item?
- What is the cost of the fastening?
- Does the fastening need to be invisible?
- Is the fastening a design feature?
- How secure does the fastening need to be?

Zips

Zips are a very popular form of fastening. They can be made from lightweight nylon available in a variety of colours and can have metal teeth for strength. Zips can be used as a design feature – large plastic teeth are often used on outdoor garments for both adults and children. Zips are available in different lengths and can be closed or open-ended.

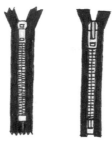

Buttons and buttonholes

Buttons are the most widely used method of fastening. They can be decorative as well as functional; some have shanks and some are flat. Buttons without shanks have two or four holes and are attached to the textile item by thread.

Toggles

Toggles can be used at the end of a drawstring and often have a spring grip to hold the cord under tension, so it does not have to be tied. They can also be used as a fastening with a cord or leather loops known as frogs.

Eyelets and lacing

This method of fastening is useful where a lacing effect is required. Holes or eyelets are made in the fabric and finished off with small stitching or with a metal eyelet. A lace is then threaded through the eyelets and tied.

Hooks and eyes

Hook and eye fasteners are a discrete form of fastening. They are often used at the top of zips to stop the garment slipping down if the zip comes undone.

Press fasteners and gingersnaps

Here, one circular piece snaps into a larger circular piece on the other side of the opening. The pieces can be made of metal or plastic and in different sizes. Press fasteners are attached using thread. Gingersnaps are attached using a special 'locking' tool.

Velcro

Velcro is made of two layers of nylon. One layer is covered with tiny hooks and the other is covered with tiny loops. When pressed together, the hooks grip the loops. Velcro can be an alternative to zips, buttons and press fasteners.

Ribbons and ties

Ribbons and ties are often used as a decorative way of fastening items. They are easy and inexpensive to use, but are not very secure.

Activities

1 List the factors that are considered when choosing a fastener.
2 List the fastenings which could also be design features.

Textile components 2

Linings

Linings are used on many textile items to:

- improve the hang or drape and reduce creasing
- improve the insulating properties
- make it easier to put on and remove, and also make it more comfortable to wear
- protect it from perspiration
- extend the life of the garment
- improve its appearance by hiding seams.

Linings for clothing

Linings must withstand the same wear and tear as the outer fabric and follow the same care procedures.

Linings for furnishings

It is usual to line curtains and other furnishings to improve wear. Curtains are also lined in order to reduce the amount of light coming through and to insulate the room. Lining in curtains must not shrink when washed or dry cleaned.

Interfacing

This is an extra layer of material placed between the outer fabric and lining. The main function is to give body and shape to the outer fabric. Interfacings are also used to keep parts of a garment stiff, e.g. collars.

Interfacings can also be the main source of insulation when they are added to textile items in the form of wadding and stitched in place, e.g. in quilted jackets.

There is a large range of interfacing materials available to satisfy the performance characteristics of all fabrics. Interfacing can be woven, knitted or bonded. They can also be sewn into a textile item or fused to the outer fabric by heat. Choice of interfacing depends on cost, design of garment and compatibility with outer fabric.

Interfacings are available in a number of weights. The choice of weight depends on the weight of the outer fabric.

Interfacing is used in shirt collars to give a stiff appearance

Wadding adds insulation to quilted jackets

Components such as boning give shape to a garment, while sequins and beads are purely decorative

Giving shape

Some textile components, such as shoulder pads, elastic and boning, give shape to a garment.

Shoulder pads

These are used to alter the shape and change the line of the shoulder in suits and coats. They are stitched between the lining and outer fabric. Some are removable, such as the ones often found in women's knitted jumpers and jackets.

Elastic

This is used to reduce fullness. Elastic can be inserted into a casing or sewn directly onto the fabric.

Boning

Boning is a strip of rigid yet flexible polyester tape, used to give structure and shape to clothing, e.g. ballgowns and basques.

Decorative components

Buttons can be both functional and decorative. Braid, fringing, feather, fur, lace and piping add interest, texture and colour and cover raw edges. Beads and sequins are often added to give colour, texture and sparkle. Embroidery can be added by hand or machine. Appliqué badges or flowers can be used to enhance the appearance.

Activities

1 Give three reasons why linings are used in textile items.
2 Sketch a textile item that makes use of decorative components.

Key points

● The majority of textile items require pre-manufactured components.
● Textile components can be functional or decorative.

Testing and trialling pre-manufactured components

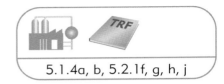
The testing and trialling of textile components can be done in a variety of ways. The main aim should be to ensure that all your testing and trialling is appropriate to the design proposal and can be justified. Textile components can be functional or decorative and are very important to the quality of the finished product. Use the following information about components here to help you with this section.

Testing and trialling thread

When testing and trialling threads the following should be considered:

- suitable colours for the fabric and the product
- suitable stitch types, e.g. stretch stitch to sew a stretch fabric
- suitable types of thread for the fabric (generally, **polyester thread** is used for sewing synthetic and stretch fabrics, **mercerized cotton thread** for cotton and linen fabrics, **pure silk thread** for silk fabrics, **viscose thread** for embroidery and **silk** or **synthetic thread** for wool fabrics, as they will give with the fabric).

A label found on thread

To test each of these ideas:

- cut two pieces of each fabric to be tested and place them together
- sew a straight line of the chosen stitch, colour or thread type; repeat this process until you have made a range of samples
- record your results in table form
- select the best type of colour, stitch or thread for the fabric type.

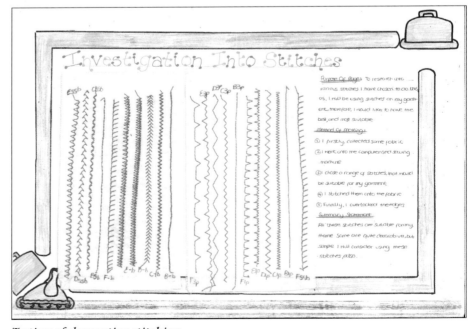

Testing of decorative stitching

Testing stitches for a specific function

Testing and trialling fastenings

When testing and trialling fastenings, test types appropriate to the design proposal – no credit is given for testing a wide range of fastenings for a textile product when only two or three are appropriate.

In industry, an individual components list is used as a basis for preparing an operations plan, for calculating fabric and accessory requirements and costs. This is an important stage in the construction of a garment. Designers take finishing and trim components seriously.

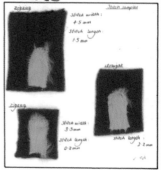

Production and materials plan with components

Production Plan: 4157

Operations plan	no: 5357
Balance plan	no: 6357
Cutting Pattern	no: 7357
Product:	boys trousers
Components:	
Description:	boys fashion trousers
with top stitched flying pockets,	
circular waistband with extension	
and hook closing, front lined.	
issued by:	date:

Components	Materials			
Top cloth:	Top Cloth	Lining	Waist band	Hooks
1 pair trousers fronts				
1 pair trousers backs				
1 pair pocket facings				
1 pair waistbands	2371	71	14	2
	2398	74	14	2
Lining:	2415	79	15	4
1 pair front trouser linings	2552	81	15	2
1 pair pockets, large				
1 pair pockets, small				
Accessories:				
80 cm waistbanding				
1 zipper, 18 cm	other accessories:		1 size label	
1 hook & eye	(6) Thread: 20/2 for attaching			
1 quality label	Thread: 100/3 for all other work			
1 care label				

Activities

1 a Make up a knitted fabric sample and test for the most suitable stitch to use.

b Describe your investigation using annotated drawings.

2 Devise and carry out simple tests to investigate thread types in relation to fabric type.

3 a List the components that could be used for fastening a textile product of your choice. Include a picture of this product.

b Describe the advantages of each.

c Devise and carry out a simple test to investigate your fastening choices.

d Record your results and give detailed reasons for your choice of fastening.

Key points

● Selection of the correct thread type gives a better quality product.

● Thread can be decorative and functional.

● Care to trimming and added finishing touches creates a professional look.

● Test and trial fastening ideas.

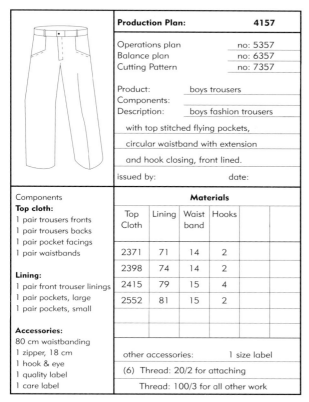

Surface decoration with fabric and thread

Appliqué

This technique involves cutting shapes out of fabric and stitching them onto a background fabric. The shapes are often backed with iron-on interfacing (see p.76) to strengthen them and prevent fraying. A close zigzag stitch is worked over the edge to attach the shape. If hand-stitching is to be used, the edge of the shape needs to be turned under to neaten it.

This technique can be used to add texture as well as to strengthen and reinforce fabrics. The shapes can be padded by making a small cut in the background fabric under the shape and pushing in filling. The cut is then oversewn to close it.

Commercial motifs can be purchased and stitched onto products in the same way. Any textile product can be decorated using **appliqué**.

Molar work, also called 'mola' or 'molas', is a form of appliqué, also called San Blas appliqué. Several layers of fabric are placed on top of each other and a design is outlined in stitching. Sections of fabric are cut away close to the stitching lines to reveal the fabric beneath.

Free machine embroidery

This technique has been developed from the process of darning, using the sewing machine. The presser foot is removed and the feed dogs disengaged. The fabric is stretched tightly in an embroidery ring, which is used upside down so that the fabric is flat on the bed of the machine.

The fabric is positioned under the machine needle and the presser foot lever is lowered to ensure correct tension on the thread. The fabric is moved around under the needle to fill the shapes of the design with stitching. Large areas can be filled with a wide zigzag stitch, while fine lines can be created using a straight stitch.

Hand embroidery

Hand embroidery is a traditional craft dating back thousands of years. A wide variety of threads is available for hand embroidery, often requiring different needles to use and of course suitable fabric to work on. There is an infinite number of stitches that can be worked. The main stitches are:

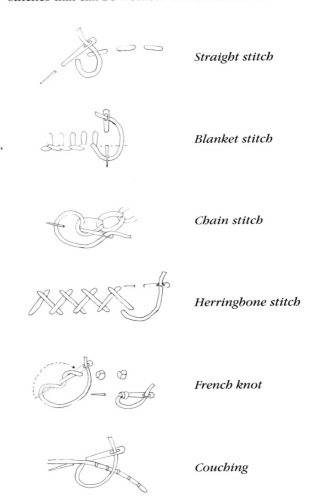

Straight stitch

Blanket stitch

Chain stitch

Herringbone stitch

French knot

Couching

Shisha work involves stitching tiny mirrors onto the fabric. It originated in India and is often seen as part of decoration. The mirrors can be purchased with the complex stitching ready worked around the edge.

Pleating and folding

These techniques are often associated with giving shape to textile products. The pleat or fold can be pressed in place using an iron, or stitched to make it permanent. Fabric can be pleated and folded to create interesting textural effects as well as functional ones.

Smocking is a traditional craft which involves regularly pleating a fabric, then working hand-stitching on the surface of the pleats.

Smocking

Decorative machine stitching

Most sewing machines have a selection of decorative stitches built in. Some electronic sewing machines can produce hundreds of different stitches with the desired one being selected by simply typing in a number corresponding to the stitch. These machines automatically set the stitch length and width.

Programmable machines allow combinations of stitch patterns to be stored in the memory. Text can be typed in and stored. Some machines allow the user to design their own stitches and programme them (see p.78).

Quilting

Quilting involves stitching three layers of fabric together. A layer of insulating fabric, such as polyester wadding, is sandwiched between a top fabric which is usually decorative and a bottom layer which is usually a cheaper fabric. If the quilting is to be reversible, the same fabric may be used for the top and bottom layers. The layers are machine stitched together, producing a fabric which has insulation and protective qualities as well as being decorative. The pattern of machine stitching and the stitch itself can be varied to create a range of effects.

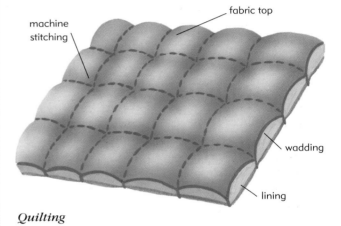

Quilting

Activities

1 Research the different forms of appliqué and quilting.

2 Collect information about computer-controlled and programmable sewing machines.

3 Work samples of the techniques described in this section.

Key point

● There are many ways to embellish a fabric using other fabrics and thread. The technique used is determined by the design to be created.

Use of modern and computerized embroidery machines

Stitching and embroidery machines are constantly changing to satisfy the demands of the manufacturer and the consumer. Machine stitching needs to be quick and easy and to offer a range of facilities to suit any type of textile product. In the classroom, the machines listed on these pages are useful tools in the development of a quality product.

Electronic sewing/ embroidery machines

An example of an electronic machine is the Memory Craft 8000 model, produced by Janome which includes a scanner facility. This allows the user to scan in designs, which the machine stores to be machine-stitched at a later stage.

pattern on memory card

drawing

scanner

stitching patterns on digital display

memory card inserted into sewing machine

pattern automatically embroidered

Scanning in facility

An original drawing can be scanned in. The drawing is then converted into stitching patterns on a digital display. The pattern is stored on a memory card. This memory card can be inserted into a sewing machine where the pattern is automatically embroidered.

Computer-aided embroidery machines

The new Janome model, the Memory Craft 10 000 can be connected to a computer and upgraded with software. It has a drag and drop editing feature that allows you to move designs around the 'touch screen' using your fingertip.

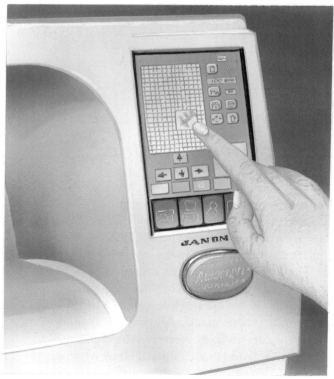

Drag and drop editing feature

Husqvarna Viking Designer I machine

Computer-aided embroidery has developed further through better software packages and technological equipment. For example, Husqvarna Viking have developed the Designer I machine, offering facilities ranging from a colour touch screen with built-in disk drive so that designs can be transferred from a PC and updated from the Internet, to built-in customizing and digitizing systems which allow the user to combine, cut or copy and paste designs on a screen and to create images from clip art files, personal drawings and photographs.

Another example of a computer-aided embroidery machine is the POEM, which can be used to transfer designs from the computer screen to the fabric through the use of special software which enables design ideas to be 'transformed' into stitches and colours. It allows other graphic packages to be used to create customized designs for the user.

A student using the POEM machine

In industry, stitching machines are also changing. Embroidery is increasingly done using the **tubular (cylinder arm) machine**, which allows the manufacturer to work directly on the made-up product. For example, this machine can be adapted for caps like the baseball cap, where logos or motifs are required to customize the product.

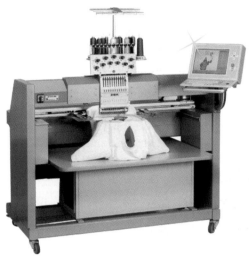

Multi-head tubular system machine used to design T-shirts

Activities

1 Make a collection of textile products that have been embellished using machine stitching. Your starting point could be the Husqvarna website: www.husqvarnaviking.com

- the range of buttonholes
- the range of utility stitches.

2 Compile a report about computerized sewing machines.

Key points

- Designs can quickly and easily be transformed from a design to a stitched pattern through the use of a computer.
- Investigations into stitch type, colour, size and pattern can be performed easily, using computerized embroidery

Colouring fabric 1

Colour can be introduced at various stages during textile production. Man-made fibres can be coloured while they are in liquid form, known as spin dyeing. Fibres can be dyed before they are spun into yarn, known as stock dyeing. The yarn can be dyed before being made into fabric. Fabric can be dyed before being used, known as piece dyeing, or garment dyeing can be done at the end of the making process. There are advantages and disadvantages to introducing colour at the different stages and the method chosen depends on the needs of the end user and the fibre or fabric being dyed. Before applying colour to any fibre or fabric it is important to remove any finishes which may have been applied during manufacture by washing.

Dyeing

This process involves immersing fibres or fabrics in liquid pigments to change their colour. The first dyestuffs came from natural sources such as plants and insects. They are known as natural dyes and are still used today. The development of synthetic dyes in 1859 made colouring fabric more predictable and greatly increased the range of colours available. They are cheaper to make than natural dyes and the colour can be matched more easily. A chemical known as a mordant is used to fix the colour to the fabric.

Tie-dye

This is one of the oldest and simplest methods of colouring fabric.

Before being placed in the dye bath, the fabric is folded and tied with string. This prevents the dye reaching some parts of the fabric, and restricts the amount absorbed in others so that a pattern is created. No two patterns are the same, and effects can be achieved by varying the folds and ties. The fabric can be dyed a number of times in different colours, and by re-folding and tying between colours, complex patterns can be achieved. It is important to remember that the colours accumulate, for example a yellow fabric placed in a blue bath will become green. Dyes are fixed by ironing. An example of tie dye is shown below.

Batik

This technique also works by making the fabric resist the dye, this time by applying wax. It originated in Indonesia on the island of Java. Batik works best on absorbent fabrics such as silk and cotton. Synthetic fabrics do not absorb the wax or the dye as easily.

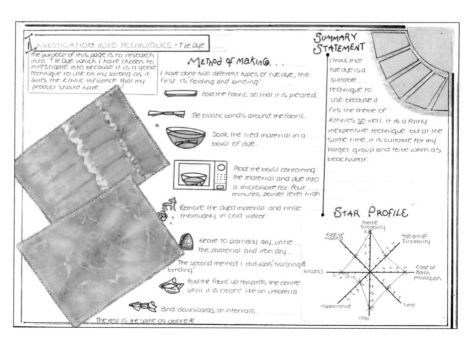

The fabric is stretched in a frame and wax applied using a **tjanting** tool (see photo on page 113) or a brush. The fabric is then immersed in a cold water dye bath for some time before being allowed to dry. More wax can be applied and the process repeated to build up the design. As with tie-dye, the colours accumulate. Lighter ones should be applied first.

At the end of the process, the wax is removed by ironing the fabric between two pieces of absorbent paper. Final traces of wax are removed by placing the fabric in boiling water for a few minutes, having fixed the colours beforehand.

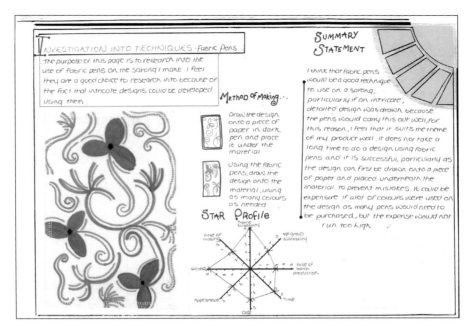

Reverse batik involves covering all the fabric with wax and then scraping off areas where the design is required. Finer designs can be achieved using this method.

Simple methods of colouring fabric

Colour can be applied simply and directly using fabric paints, crayons and marker pens (see student example above). The design is drawn on the fabric using a tailor's pencil and then coloured. These are very simple methods and do not require much equipment. The colours are fixed by ironing.

Spraying

Immersing fabric in a dye bath produces a solid colour. A speckled effect can be achieved by spraying the dye on the surface of the fabric using a spray diffuser or an airbrush. Areas can be masked off using a stencil, or the colours can be blended together to produce a soft effect.

Activities

1. Produce a sample of each of the methods of colouring fabric.
2. Use the Internet to research methods of colouring fabric by other cultures.

Key points

- Colour can be introduced at any stage in the production of a textile item.
- A wide range of different effects can be achieved, depending on the method used and the type of fibre or fabric being coloured.

Colouring fabric 2

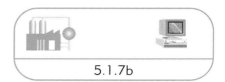

Screen printing

This is the most widely used method of printing on fabric. A fine mesh fabric is stretched tightly over a wooden frame. The dye is moved across the screen using a squeegee, which forces the dye through the screen to the fabric beneath.

Students working on a project for Cloth of Gold, a London based arts organization exploring both traditional and new creative technologies

The screen is then washed and the unexposed chemical is removed, allowing the dye through the screen. An alternative method is to apply an insoluble polymer to the screen that is etched away where the design is by a computer-controlled laser beam.

Whichever method is used to create the design, a separate screen is needed for each colour. The screen has to be large enough to cover the design area.

In industry, the length of fabric is laid out on a flat surface and stuck down using adhesive. The screen is moved on a conveyer, a screen-width at a time. The printing ink is applied and the process repeated. Alternatively, the rotary method is used which allows continual production. A cylindrical screen is used which has reservoirs inside to hold the printing ink. The ink is pumped through to the screen and spread on the moving fabric by a blade or roller squeegee. This is the quickest form of screen printing.

For one-off prints, areas of the screen can be blocked off using paper stencils placed between the screen and the fabric. For a longer run, areas of the screen are permanently blocked off. This can be done in a number of ways. One way is to coat the screen with a light-sensitive chemical. Areas that need to be blocked off are exposed to ultraviolet light which makes the chemical insoluble.

T-shirt silk screening factory in California

Block printing

A block is made of resistant material, usually wood. The design is marked on the surface, and the areas around the designs are cut away to leave the design in relief. Dye is then applied to the surface of the block, which is then pressed onto the fabric. Each colour needs its own block, and great care has to be taken to align the blocks correctly.

Use of a traditional hand-carved block for printing on fabric

Roller printing

This is the industrial development of block printing. Rollers with a copper surface are engraved with the design, the design being in relief. The maximum width of the design is the width of the roller, and the circumference of it fixes the repeat. A separate roller is needed for each colour. The expense of making the roller means that this method is only used if large amounts of fabric are to be printed.

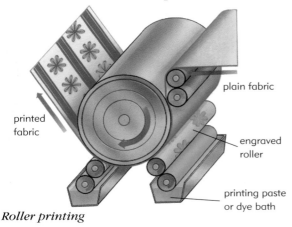

printed fabric

plain fabric

engraved roller

printing paste or dye bath

Roller printing

Transfer printing

This technique involves printing the reversed design on paper first, then transferring the design to the fabric using heat. In the classroom, transfer printing inks or crayons can be used. Alternatively, the design can be produced on the computer, and special paper fed into the printer. In each case, the print is placed face down on the fabric and ironed with a hot iron to transfer the ink from the paper to the fabric.

In industry, the design is transferred using heated rollers. The heat converts the dye on the paper to a gas which, as a result of the heat and pressure from the roller, attaches to the fabric. This process is most effective in synthetics.

Less common printing methods

Flock printing involves printing adhesive on the fabric, and then covering the fabric with cut fibre snippets.

Colour can be removed from plain dyed fabric by the application of a paste that removes or changes the colour of the dye. This is known as discharge printing.

In resist printing, parts of the fabric are printed with a resist paste which prevents the fabric from absorbing dye.

Activity

1 Compile a chart to show the advantages and disadvantages of each method of colouring fabric described on pp.84–7. Consider the implications for mass production.

Key points

- A wide range of printing methods are used in industry.
- The method used will depend on the type of fabric to be coloured, the amount to be printed and the effect required.

Industrial methods of dyeing

Dyeing involves the use of water and an additive, like salt or other chemicals, which is used to 'keep the dye' in the fabric or 'fix' it, so that the dye does not disappear when washed. There are three main types of industrial dye processes:

1 Continuous dyeing, also known as **pad dyeing** – This is where the whole of the fabric is placed into a small pad bath with the dye and is gently squeezed to ensure that the colour is evenly spread throughout the fabric.

2 Semi-continuous dyeing – This is where the fabric is dyed and then wound up on a batching roller to remove excess dye and allow the dye to fix into the fabric.

3 Batch dyeing – This is where the fabric is placed in a dye bath and allowed to absorb the colour. This method relies upon the exact weighing of the fabric and the dye in order to get a successful all-over colour.

It is useful to know about the different types of industrial dyeing processes listed above. However, it is more important to understand how products and fabrics may be dyed in batches.

Batch dyeing

Batch dyeing can be done using the jigger system, the winch system, or the jet-dying process.

The jigger system

This is where the fabric is pulled backwards and forwards through the dye bath. This makes sure that the colour is evenly spread throughout the complete batch of fabric. This process is most successful with medium- to heavy-weight woven fabrics, for example a twill fabric.

The winch system

This is where a winch pulls the fabric from the front of the dye bath through to the back in a circular movement. This process is most suitable for knitted fabrics and light-weight woven fabrics like silk.

The jigger system of batch dyeing

The jet-dyeing process

This is where the fabric is moved around the dye bath through the use of high pressure jets. This process is useful when dyeing carpets to create a multi-coloured design, where each jet is controlled by a computer to inject dye at certain positions on the carpet.

Dyeing and the environment

Developments within the dyeing industry have been motivated by:

- the need to reduce pollution in the environment

- the need to become more efficient in dyeing products and fabrics, and therefore more cost-effective.

Thermo-chromic dyes used as a fun fashion feature

The main areas of concern to a dyeing company are water and air pollution. Legislation is in place to try to ensure the proper handling of hazardous chemicals, emissions and waste.

Super-critical fluids, such as liquid carbon dioxide, are an example of recent dyeing developments used to reduce waste levels, particularly within water, use of chemicals and dyestuffs.

Thermo-chromic dyes are being used in the design of T-shirts to warn the user of any danger through over exposure to ultraviolet light or excessive heat. This is indicated by a colour change in the dye and is particularly successful in warning the user of potential skin cancer risks through spending too much time in the sun.

Activities

1 List three examples of medium- or heavy-weight fabrics suitable for dyeing using the jigger system.

2 Explain why it is important to care for the environment, and show how the dyeing industry is helping.

Key points

- The dyeing process involves the dispersal of dyes in water.

- The choice of an industrial dyeing process depends upon the type and weight of the fabric or fibre.

Finishes to fibres and fabrics

Finishes can be applied to fibres, yarns, fabrics or completed products. These finishes can be physical or chemical processes which improve the fabric in some way, e.g.:

- the look
- the feel
- the wear.

Physical finishes

Physical finishes such as brushing and calendering are applied by a mechanical action which changes the surface of the fabric.

Brushing

This technique raises the fibres on the surface of the fabric. The fabric is passed round a series of wire-covered rollers which pull up the fibre ends to form a pile. This gives a soft, fluffy surface to the fabric, and as air is trapped in the fibres the fabric is warm to wear. There are two main disadvantages to this finish. One is that the fabric is more flammable, due to the additional air held in the fabric. The second is that the fabric can be weakened by the action of the rollers. This finish is applied to cotton bedding as well as garments.

Calendering

This is the opposite of brushing. The fabric is passed between heated rollers which smooth and compact the surface of the fabric, improving its lustre (shine). The final effect can be varied by changing the surface, temperature and speed of the rollers. Although this is a durable finish, it is not permanent.

An example of a fabric with this finish is chintz, often used for furnishing fabric. The fabric is impregnated with resin before being calendered to make it firm as well as lustrous. If the rollers are engraved, a moiré (water-marked) or embossed fabric is created.

Chemical finishes

Mercerizing

This process makes cotton fibres and fabrics more lustrous. They are treated in sodium hydroxide while being held under tension. The cotton fibres become more rounded and straighter, making them softer, stronger and more absorbent. The finish is permanent and is often applied to sewing threads. It is also used on dress and shirt fabrics as well as furnishing fabrics.

Waterproofing

Chemicals, usually silicones, are applied to the fabric by spraying or by **impregnation**. This forms a barrier to prevent water droplets from soaking into the fabric. The effectiveness and durability of the finish depends on the chemicals used and the methods of application. The finish can be applied before the fabric is made into the product or afterwards. It is invisible and can be renewed. Outdoor clothing needs to be waterproof, as do umbrellas, tents and awnings.

Flame proofing

Chemicals are applied to the yarn or the fabric which slow down or prevent burning, e.g. Proban. These finishes make the fabric stiffer, and to maintain the finish, they need to be washed in accordance with the manufacturer's instructions. Any fabric can be flame-proofed. It is a particularly important finish for furnishing fabrics, especially if used in public places.

Stain resistance

The aim is to prevent the fabric from absorbing stain or dirt. Silicone treatment will resist water-based stains, while synthetic resins are needed for oil-based stains. This treatment also makes the fabric waterproof to a certain extent.

Waterproof garments

Water droplets on the surface of a waterproof fabric

Scotchguard is an example of a commercial finish. Most fabrics can be treated, e.g. furnishing fabrics, floor coverings, shoes and clothing.

Easy care

Chemicals can be applied to fabrics to make them easier to wash and iron. After treatment, the fibres do not absorb water easily so they dry quickly. They also crease less and do not shrink. Items made from cotton and viscose fibres can be treated, particularly when they are made into garments which are frequently washed.

Antistatic

Synthetic fibres can build up an electrostatic charge, causing the fabric to cling and attract dust and dirt. An antistatic finish can be given by applying chemicals to the fabric, which help the fibres absorb moisture from the atmosphere. This improves the surface conductivity and prevents the build-up of static. This is particularly useful for floor coverings and clothing such as underwear and lingerie.

Anti-felting

Wool fibres 'felt' or matt together if not washed correctly. Two methods can be used to reduce this. One is to soften the tips of the scales on the fibres by an oxidative treatment, the other is to coat the fibre with a synthetic polymer film.

Activity

1 Select the most appropriate finish for the following products, giving reasons for your choice:
   a furnishing fabric for a hotel
   b a ball gown
   c a mechanic's overalls
   d a carpet in a reception area.

Key points

- Fibres and fabrics can be finished by mechanical or chemical methods.
- Finishes improve the fabric in some way, either the look, the wear or the feel.

Joining fabrics

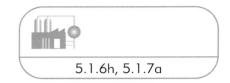
There are temporary and permanent ways of joining fabrics.

Temporary Methods

- Pins can be used to hold fabrics together while a permanent join is made, or to hold a component in place while it is attached to the product. Parts of a product may be pinned together to check that they fit properly, or that the product itself is the correct size. They are sometimes used to hold a product in place for packaging.

- Tacking can be done by hand or machine. The stitches are usually 1 cm long and often worked in a cheap, relatively weak, thread. This is a slightly more secure and less bulky method than pinning. The stitches are removed after the parts have been permanently joined.

- Fastenings are used to allow sections to be temporarily joined while the product is being used (see p.74–5).

Permanent methods of joining fabrics

Two pieces of fabric are usually joined using a seam. The choice of seam depends on a number of factors:

- the type of fabric
- the end use of the product
- the position and purpose of the seam
- ease of manufacture.

Commercially produced patterns usually allow 1.5 cm for seams, known as the **seam allowance**. When joining fabric together the stitching should be 1.5 cm from the edge of the fabric.

Any variation will result in the product being larger or smaller than intended. This ensures a quality outcome (see pp.124–7). In industry the seam allowance is usually smaller than 1.5 cm, to save fabric and therefore cost.

The plain or open seam

This is the most common seam. It is a flat seam which can be easily altered. The fabrics are placed right sides together, with the edges level then pinned. If the pins are placed at right angles to the stitching line, the machine will stitch over them. The stitching line can be marked using a tailor's pencil to ensure accuracy. Some machines have a guide marked to indicate where the edge of the fabric should be positioned to stitch 1.5 cm in from the edge. Alternatively the seam can be tacked. Once machine-stitched, the loose threads should be cut close to the fabric, and the seam pressed open. The raw edges of the seam will need to be neatened to prevent fraying and prolong the life of the product (see p.96). This seam is used on most textile items, including household textiles and clothing.

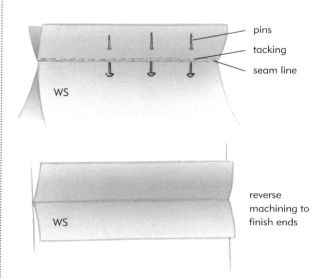

The double-stitched seam

Sometimes known as a flat-fell seam, this is a very strong seam as it is stitched twice and all of the raw edges are enclosed. The two rows of stitching form a decorative feature. The fabric is placed wrong sides together, pinned, tacked and machined 1.5 cm from the edge of the fabric. The seam is pressed open, and one side trimmed to 5 mm. The other side is folded inwards 5 mm, and then pressed over the trimmed side. The folded edge is then pinned and tacked through all thicknesses, before being machine-stitched.

A longer machine stitch is often used to accommodate thick layers. A contrasting colour of thread adds to decoration. The seam is often used on jeans and overalls. As the seam is flat, it is also used on pyjamas.

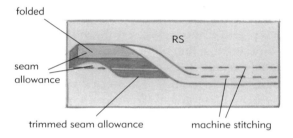

folded

RS

seam allowance

trimmed seam allowance　　machine stitching

The French seam

This seam also encloses all raw edges of the fabric and is strong as it is stitched twice. The fabric is placed wrong sides together, pinned and tacked 1 cm from the raw edge. The seam is pressed open, and trimmed to between 3 and 5 mm. The fabric is then folded so that the right sides are together, with the join previously made exactly on the fold. The fabric is then pinned, tacked and machine stitched on the original seam line, 5 mm from the edge. This seam is used on fine, sheer fabrics, e.g. lingerie, as no raw edges are visible.

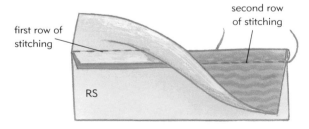

first row of stitching

second row of stitching

RS

The overlaid seam

Stitching is visible from the right side of the product and forms a decorative feature. The fabric to be overlaid has the seam allowance folded to the wrong side along the stitching line. The folded edge is then placed on the stitching line of the underlaid piece, before being pinned and tacked in position. The seam is edge-stitched close to the folded edge from the right side of the fabric. The seam is pressed, and the raw edges trimmed to 1 cm. The edges need to be neatened to prevent fraying. This seam is used to join a yoke piece on a shirt or blouse. A contrasting thread adds extra detail.

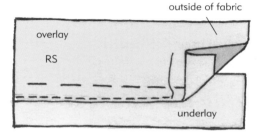

outside of fabric

overlay

RS

underlay

Activities

1 State the most suitable seam for each of the following items, and justify your choice:

　a　a square cushion

　b　a set of overalls

　c　a blouse made from organdie.

2 Why do the raw edges of seams need neatening?

3 Explain the factors to be considered when deciding which seam to use.

Key points

● Pinning, tacking and fastenings are temporary ways of joining fabric.

● Machine stitching is used to join fabric permanently using a seam.

Shaping and reducing fullness

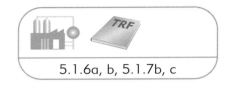

Textile items often need to be three-dimensional as in the case of garments, seat covers or toys. When making fabric into curved or irregular shapes, excess fabric or *fullness* needs to be taken out of a piece of fabric to reduce its size in places. There are several ways of doing this:

- cut the fabric to a suitable shape
- make darts in the fabric
- put tucks or pleats in the fabric
- gather the fabric.

The method used will depend on the product, the fabric and the effect required.

Cutting the fabric to shape

The diagram below shows the pattern pieces needed to make the crown section of a baseball cap. The shapes are wider at the lower edge to fit the head, and taper towards the top. When the pieces are stitched together, they curve to match the shape of the head.

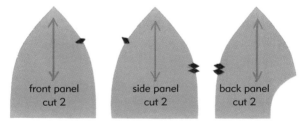

front panel cut 2

side panel cut 2

back panel cut 2

Darts

The principal behind a dart is that a triangular section of fabric is removed by stitching. This means that the rest of the fabric does not lie flat. Darts usually start where a seam is to be made and then taper to a point.

Commercial patterns indicate the position of darts with 'dots' on the pattern. Tailor tacks are worked to transfer the position of the dart to the fabric (see p.101). In industry, there may be a hole in the card pattern. A drill hole, hot-drill marker or fluorescent dye transfers the mark.

WS

The dart is formed by matching the dots together, folding along the centre of the dart with the right side of the fabric together. The fabric is pinned together and tacked starting at the wide end, tapering to a fine point. The dart is then machine-stitched, using a straight stitch. Darts are useful in waistlines, and for busts of dresses and blouses. Double-pointed darts occur where two darts are joined together, like in a one-piece dress. This type is snipped at its widest point, at the waistline, to make it lie flat.

Tucks and pleats

These are folds in the fabric. They can be pressed in place or machine-stitched for a more permanent effect. They are used at sleeve heads, the wrist and the waist and on valances, and are a decorative way of removing fullness.

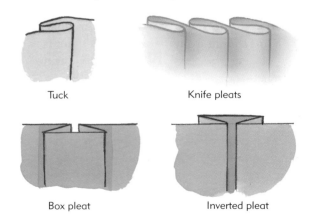

Tuck

Knife pleats

Box pleat

Inverted pleat

Gathers

This involves working one or two rows of stitching, which are pulled up to form a series of tiny tucks. Stitching can be done by hand or machine. If large lengths of fabric need to be gathered, it is best to work in smaller sections to reduce the risk of the threads breaking. Alternatively, a gathering or ruffler attachment can be used on the machine.

Gathers are a popular method of disposal of fullness, used at the waistband, sleeve heads, cuffs and on frills and yokes.

By machine

The machine is set to work a long straight stitch. Some machines recommend loosening the top thread tension to make it easier to pull up the lower threads.

The first row of stitching is worked on the seam line where the fabric needs to be gathered. The thread should not be fastened on or off, but left with the ends hanging. A second row of stitching is worked between the first row and the edge of the fabric, inside the seam allowance.

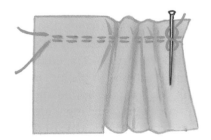

The threads can then be pulled up from both ends of the stitching to gather the fabric by the required amount. The ends of the threads are secured in a figure of eight around pins. The gathers then need to be distributed evenly. The fabric is then ready to be joined.

By hand

This is best worked using double machine thread that matches the fabric. The process is the same as for gathering by machine, but a small running stitch is worked by hand rather than by machine.

Other methods

Elastic inside a casing can shape a product. A casing is a tube formed in the fabric which the elastic is threaded into. This can be used at the waist or at the bottom of a sleeve as it not only shapes the fabric but also allows the garment to be put on and taken off easily.

Rufflet tape is used on curtains to gather them to fit the window, and adds a design feature.

Smocking is also a decorative method of shaping products.

Activities

1 Produce a table which summarizes the methods of disposal of fullness. Illustrate each method with a sketch and indicate where it might be used.

2 Collect pictures of textile products from magazines and catalogues to illustrate each method of shaping and reducing fullness.

Key points

- Many textile products need to be shaped to dispose of fullness.
- Some methods are purely functional while others add a decorative feature.
- The method used to shape or reduce fullness depends on the product, the effect required and the fabric used.

Edge finishes and hems

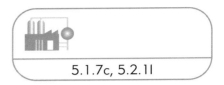

Cut edges of fabric need to be finished in some way. All woven fabrics fray to some extent and weft-knitted fabric unravels. Although warp-knitted fabrics and bonded fabrics do not come undone, the edges do lose their shape and curl spoiling the finished effect.

Even when the cut edges have been incorporated into a seam, if the edge of the fabric is visible on the inside of the product, it should be neatened.

The method of neatening used will depend on:

- the type of fabric
- the position of the seam or edge
- the product.

Neatening edges on a plain seam

When the seam has been pressed open, the edges can be treated in a number of ways. The edge of the fabric can be turned under 5 mm and the turning held in place by a row of straight or zigzag stitching.

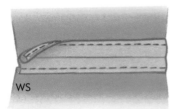

The edge of the fabric can be zigzagged without turning it under.

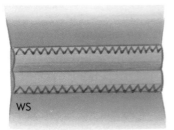

If the seam is not pressed open, (e.g. the seam inside a cushion), the edges can be trimmed and zigzagged together.

Overlockers

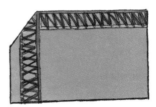

This machine streamlines the process of making and neatening a seam. The overlocker stitches the seam, neatens the edge and trims off the excess fabric all in one operation. This method of making and neatening a seam is particularly suitable for stretch fabrics as there is a certain amount of give in the seam which reduces the risk of the threads snapping during use (see p.117).

This method of neatening can be used on any raw edge: it is not limited to use on a plain seam.

Bias binding

This is a narrow strip of fabric cut on the bias of a woven fabric (see p.51). The edges are folded under and pressed in place. The slight stretch means that it can be applied to curved edges without wrinkling, making it a good way to finish edges such as armholes. One of the folded edges is opened out and the crease placed on the stitching line, right sides together. This is pinned and tacked in place and machine-stitched in the crease. The binding is turned to the inside, or wrong side, of the product, with the join on the edge. The free edge of the binding is hand-stitched in place.

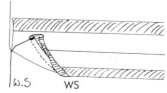

Seam neatened using bias binding

To form a more decorative, visible finish, the binding can be applied so that it can be seen from the right side of the product. In this case, the seam allowance needs to be trimmed to suit the width of the binding, ensuring the finished neatened edge is on the fitting line. This method might be used on the lower edge of an oven mitt (see p.16).

Facings

Edges can be neatened invisibly using a facing. This is a piece of fabric cut to match the shape of the edge to be neatened. They are then used to finish necklines, openings and waists.

The shape is usually cut from the same fabric as the product, although it can be cut from a lining to reduce bulk. **Interfacing** is usually applied to strengthen and stiffen the facing to maintain shape (see pp.76–7). The edges of the facing which are not to be attached to the product need to be neatened.

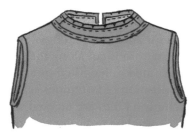

The edges of the facing are then lined up with the edge to be neatened and pinned and tacked in place. A straight machine stitch attaches the facing, the stitching being worked on the seam line. The seam is then trimmed to reduce bulk, and if it is curved, small V-shaped sections will need to be cut out of the seam allowance to enable the facing to lie flat. The facing is secured to the inside of the product by hand stitching, or understitched by machine.

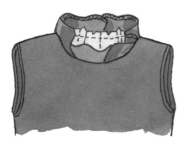

Hems

The type of hem worked depends upon the fabric and the style of the product. The hem is often worked by machine rather than by hand.

Rolled hems are usually narrow and made by folding the fabric twice so that the raw edge is invisible. The raw edge is turned to the inside, around 5 mm. This can be secured by pressing, or by straight or zigzag machine-stitching. The hem is then folded in again by about the same amount and stitched in place by machine (straight stitch) or hand (herringbone stitch or slip hemming). This type of hem can only be worked on medium- to light-weight fabrics.

For thicker fabrics, or where there is tapered fullness, a single fold hem is more appropriate. The raw edge can be finished by a zigzag stitch worked over the edge, or by overlocking. The hem is then turned to the inside and secured by hand sewing or a machine hemming stitch. Fullness is pleated or gathered to ensure the hem lies flat.

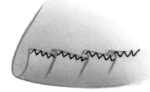

Bondaweb is a soft, fusible fleece used to secure hems. It is placed between the turned-up hem and the main fabric, and pressed with an iron. The fleece melts and glues the hem.

Activity

1 Draw up a table of the advantages and disadvantages of each edge finish.

Key points

● Cut, raw edges are almost always neatened in some way to prevent fraying and improve the quality of the product.

● The way in which the edge is finished depends on the fabric and on the position of the edge.

Patterns 1

Paper patterns are often used when making textile products. They enable complex shapes to be cut from fabric accurately, improving the quality of the product.

Commercial patterns

Commercial patterns can be bought from shops. The patterns have been tested to ensure they work and fit together. They consist of three main parts: the pattern pieces, an instruction sheet and an envelope.

The envelope shows the product(s) that can be made using the pattern and gives information about suitable fabrics. There is also a list of other components needed such as thread, buttons and zips. If it is a garment, there will usually be a body measurement chart to work out which size should be made.

The pattern pieces are printed on thin tissue paper. These are pinned on the fabric and cut round. There is a lot of information on each piece to aid cutting and assembly. Much of this information is in the form of symbols.

The pattern pieces are printed on a large sheet of paper. The cutting line indicates where the edges of the pattern pieces are. The straight grain arrow must be placed on the straight grain of the fabric, parallel to the selvedge (see p.50). The place on fold arrow indicates that the edge of the pattern piece needs to be exactly on a fold of fabric. The fabric is not cut along that edge. The notches have two purposes: (i) for matching the pieces together, to indicate how they fit, and (ii) to identify the pieces by the position and number of notches.

The stitching line indicates where the stitching should be worked when joining fabric. The seam allowance is the distance between the cutting line and the stitching line, usually 1.5 cm. on a commercial pattern. Dots indicate positions of darts and pockets, (see p.101) which need to be transferred to the fabric. Lengthen or shorten lines are used for altering the length of a garment. The pattern is cut along the lines and the pieces separated to lengthen or folded to shorten. The position of fastenings such as buttons and button holes are marked with a symbol. The centre line indicates the middle of the pattern piece.

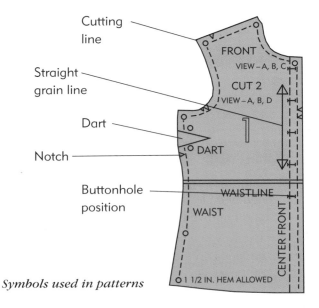

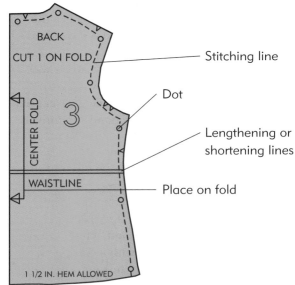

Symbols used in patterns

Making patterns

Patterns for garments are developed from basic blocks, pattern pieces used to make a garment that exactly fits the body. They come in standard body sizes to set measurements.

When a design is produced, these basic blocks are adapted. A basic block pattern is produced for each section of a garment, including the bodice, sleeve, etc. Block patterns are produced for men's, women's and children's clothing.

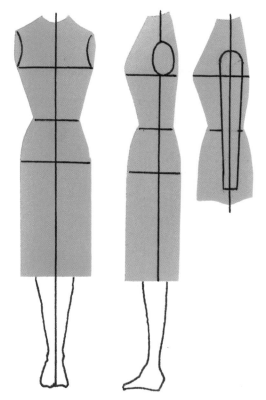

Basic block patterns

Drawing out these patterns takes a lot of time, involving complex calculations. This can now be done using a computer. Data can be entered and saved and the computer will draw out the blocks. Personal measurements can also be entered to produce a customized pattern.

An example of a program used in schools is 'Fittingly Sew'. This can be used to adapt the pattern for a new garment design, which can be done quickly and accurately with a computer. The pattern can be stored on the computer.

Grading patterns

When a pattern has been adapted, it will be graded. This means making adjustments to the pattern to make it fit larger and smaller sizes. Grading can be seen when a multi-size commercial pattern is used.

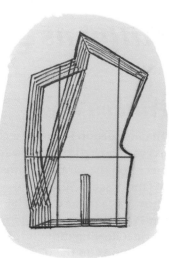

A pattern piece showing how different sizes have been added to 'grade' the pattern

This is also done on a computer which calculates the grading and adds it to the pattern piece. Various sizes are nested on one pattern piece, or each size can be drawn out separately.

The patterns produced can be plotted on paper, or a more durable material for manual cutting. Marks to be transferred to the fabric are often marked as holes in the paper and transferred (see p.94). In a fully automated system, the information produces a lay plan (see p.100) that is sent directly to the cutting machine.

Activities

1 Study a commercial pattern. Identify the points mentioned in this section.

2 Find out how commercial patterns are adapted to produce a few styles of garment from one basic pattern shape.

Key points

● Making a pattern for a garment is a complex task. This is made much easier and more accurate if a computer is used.

● Patterns are not only used to make garments, but also other textile products.

Patterns 2

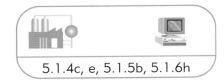
Pattern lays

The instruction sheet for a commercial pattern has diagrams to show how to arrange the pattern pieces on the various widths of fabric (see p.50). This is known as a pattern lay. The pattern is arranged on the fabric following the instructions on the pattern piece, e.g. the straight grain arrow or place on fold arrow.

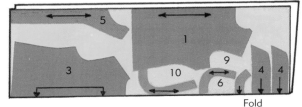

Layout for a fabric 115 cm wide

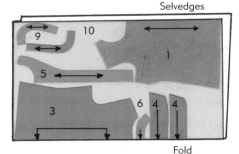

Layout for a fabric 150 cm wide

Producing a pattern lay

This can be done by arranging the pattern pieces on the fabric manually, moving them around until the minimum amount of fabric is used. Either the full-size patterns or scaled models can be used. This method is suitable for one product, but it is not practical for a large number.

Pattern lays in industry

It is particularly important to fit the pattern pieces as closely together as possible as this reduces the amount of fabric wasted, therefore reducing costs. One method is to arrange the pattern pieces for a number of garments on the fabric all at once, saving time and fabric. Another way is to arrange the pattern pieces for more than one size on the fabric. This is known as mixed multi-size lay.

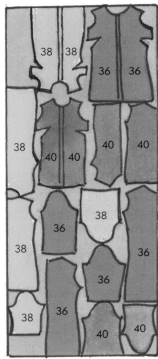

Mixed multi-size lay with different shades showing different sizes

Fabric is rarely folded in industry. Pattern lays are usually arranged on single, flat fabric. Folding the fabric uses more than does using it flat. Pattern pieces are made for the right and left side of the garment. The main exception is when tubular knitted fabric is used as this is already doubled over.

Computerization

The pieces can be moved around on screen until the optimum layout is achieved. Some systems do this automatically. The finished plan is stored or printed out on full-size or scaled-down paper. With CAD/CAM systems there is no need for a paper pattern, as the cutting instructions are sent directly to the cutting machine. The fabric is cut using a knife, laser beam, high-energy plasma or high-pressure water jet.

Pinning on and cutting out

Pin the pattern piece at the top and bottom of the grain line to hold it in place whilst the remainder of the pattern is pinned. If the fabric has checks or stripes, ensure that these will match at the seams. Any large design on the fabric is placed so that it is centred on the front and back pieces and placed suitably on the sleeves (usually middle centre front).

Fabric should be folded according to the instructions on the pattern. It is usual to place the right side of the fabric to the inside of the fold to protect it from getting marked during cutting and preparing. When all the pattern pieces have been placed on the fabric, pin them firmly in place using pins 10–12 cm. apart and facing outwards, but not overlapping the pattern edges! Cut out the pattern pieces carefully, cutting out all notches or balance marks outwards from the edge.

Marking out the pattern pieces

Information about how to make the product is listed on the pattern pieces and needs to be transferred accurately and securely to the fabric, for example with tailor's chalk (available in white, pink and mustard yellow) specifically designed marker pens, or by **Tailors Tacking**.

The wrong side of the fabric should also be marked using tailor's chalk or pencil, so that it is clear where to position the tack.

1 Thread a needle with a long double length of thread in a contrasting colour to the fabric. Make a stitch through the dot on the pattern and through both layers of fabric, going in one side of the dot and out on the other. Leave a long end of thread (about 4 cm).

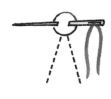

2 Make another stitch in exactly the same place, again going through both layers of fabric and the pattern, to form a loop of thread which should be about 4 cm.

3 Cut the threads leaving ends of about 4 cm, then cut the loop. This creates four threads on either side of the dot.

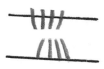

4 Remove the paper pattern. Ease the two layers of fabric apart and carefully cut the threads between the fabrics, leaving threads in both pieces.

How a tailor's tack is made using a simple stitch with a double thread

Activities

1 Produce a worked example of a tailor's tack. Mount this sample on a piece of paper or in your notebook.

2 Produce a flow chart explaining how you made your tailor's tack.

3 Explain why this is an effective way to mark a fabric.

Key points

● A commercial pattern is a ready-made set of paper templates from which a textile product can be made.

● Tailor's tacking is a temporary stitching technique used to mark the fabric.

Patterns and prototypes

Allowing extra fabric

Sometimes it is not possible to fit the pattern pieces closely together because of the nature of the fabric. Fabric which has a striped or checked design needs to be cut out carefully so that when the pieces are stitched together, the design matches and the effect shown below is avoided.

The notches can be used to line up the pattern pieces correctly on the design, but this will result in wastage of fabric, as the pieces cannot be placed as closely together. In this case, matching the design on the product is more important than saving fabric to ensure a quality product. The extra costs involved will be passed on to the customer.

The fabric shown below has a one-way design. All of the butterflies are the same way up on the fabric.

The pattern pieces need to be placed on the fabric so that when the product is made, all the butterflies are the right way up. This means more fabric will be used as the pieces have to be arranged to suit the design on the fabric, rather than just fitting them closely together. The wastage needs to be allowed for when planning and costing the fabric.

The same principal applies to fabric which has a nap or pile such as velvet or corduroy (see p.53). The light reflects off the surface differently depending on which way the pile is lying. The pattern pieces need to be arranged so that the pile lies in the same direction from top to toe of the garment, to ensure consistency of colour.

Quilting fabric

If a fabric is to be quilted it is important to make an allowance for the quilting process. Stitching the three layers together causes the fabric to shrink in size, with the finished piece of quilting being smaller than the pre-quilted fabrics. The amount of shrinkage depends on the thickness of the insulation layer and the density of the stitching.

There are two ways to make a product from quilted fabric. One is to quilt the fabric before laying on the pattern pieces so that the shrinkage has already taken place. However, quilting a large piece of fabric by machine can be difficult and time-consuming.

An alternative is to cut the fabric to size and shape first, and then quilt the individual pieces. This involves cutting the three layers separately, and they will need to be cut bigger to allow for shrinkage. This can be quite wasteful in terms of fabric and time.

More information on quilting can be found on p.81.

The importance of the toile or prototype

Within the classroom a **toile**, mock-up or **prototype** of the design proposal can be used to test different ideas alongside the size, drape and fit. A toile can be successfully made from recycled fabric and pattern or tracing paper to give a realistic look of how the design proposal will take shape.

Industry use of protoypes

In industry prototypes are widely use. Samples of each chosen style in the collection are cut and sewn in the sample room, usually using a cheap fabric (calico) to make garment prototypes. Fabric is used rather than paper because it is more realistic. Mannequins in the shape of the body are used to see how the product fits and shapes. Initial costings for material, labour and appropriate profit margins are calculated and compared with street prices.

The prototypes are then tested for sales appeal, using surveys, questionnaires and one-to-one discussion, and if necessary they are modified at the second appraisal stage. This is done by the designer and toile maker, who work closely together. Styles which lack appeal are either eliminated or have their design features changed to meet the needs of the customer/user.

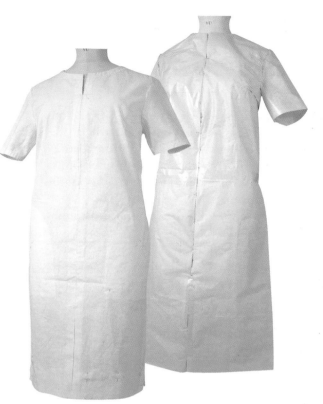

Toiles made of calico (left) and paper (right) are used to establish the final shape of the product

The designer corrects such changes to their satisfaction and then produces a sample garment in the chosen fabric. This is shown to the manufacturer or to the retailers before full-scale production begins.

In the fashion world, these trial garments need to be of a high quality as they will be viewed (via fashion shows) by retailers who will place orders for the completed products.

Activities

1 Make a collection of fabrics that have a nap or a pile.

2 Explain why products made from these fabrics are more expensive to produce.

3 Explain the use a toile has within the design process.

4 How can a toile or prototype be tested? Design a survey or questionnaire to explain your answer.

Key points

● When using fabrics with a pile or a nap, extra fabric is needed.

● Quilting a fabric causes it to shrink in size.

● A toile does not have to be made of the complete design proposal; areas of the product may be modelled, e.g. a range of pocket styles, a collar or a cuff detail.

The final product specification

After deciding upon which materials, production methods and pre-manufactured standard components are the most suitable for the textile product, it is important that all of your decisions and choices are collated and full details about the final product given.

The most successful way to do this is through the use of a product or manufacturing specification. This specification will be the basis of all the manufacturing processes to follow so it needs to be very detailed. You could complete a manufacturing specification in a variety of ways:

- *chart format* – using text and basic drawings to explain all relevant details

- *working information sheet* – combining text with design and modelling techniques to explain all relevant details

- *written/text format* – writing down all the relevant details with explanations as to choice.

ICT could be used to scan design details onto a specification chart, or you could desk top publish data onto the specification. You could also scan in details of the individual components and fabric swatches or produce text to help enforce the presentation.

If you have analysed your previous investigations thoroughly and given detailed explanations as to the final choice of each material and component, then there is no need to repeat the process of evaluation in this section.

The manufacturing/product specification is a visual or written summary of all your decisions.

In industry, a product specification takes the form of a production plan – this includes a description of the product, lists all of the components needed and provides information on the materials to be used and their quantities.

Cost Sheet

Customers Name: Jurassic Clothing
Description: fleece waistcoat
Date: 18/11/99
Age/Size: 3 - 4 years

Sketch

Fabric Swatches

Front view | Back View

Garment Cost		Quality & Colour	Supplier of component	Amount used	Price per unit	Total
Main fabric 100% Polyester		Lime fleece	Boyes Stores	50cm	£3.99	£2.00
Other fabrics						
Lining						
Interlining						
Zips	Navy	12" Open Ended	Boyes Stores	1		£1.50
Threads	Navy	100% polyester	100m = £1.00	10m	£1.00	£0.10
Buttons						
Other trimmings	Thread	Embroidery Blue	8m = £0.20	4m	£0.20	£0.10
Clients Label		Jurassic Clothing	Clients own	1		£0.08
Wash care label		Hand wash	Morplan	1		£0.01
Fibre content label		100% polyester	Morplan	1		£0.01
Other labels		Made in England	Morplan	1		£0.01
Swing Ticket		Jurassic clothing	Clients own	1		£0.05
Bag/Hanger/delivery		Folded in Clear polythene bag		1		£0.20
Component total						£4.06
Wastage + 10%		10 cm at £3.99 per metre			£0.399	£0.44
Cut & Make		1 hour to cut & make at £5.50 per hour				£5.50
Manufacturing total						£10.00
Overheads + 100%		Gas, Electric, Phone,etc.			£1.00	£2.00
Wholesale Selling price						£12.00
Retail selling price + 150%		Round figure to nearest 99p			£30.00	£29.99

An example of a piece of student training material showing the format of an industrial production plan

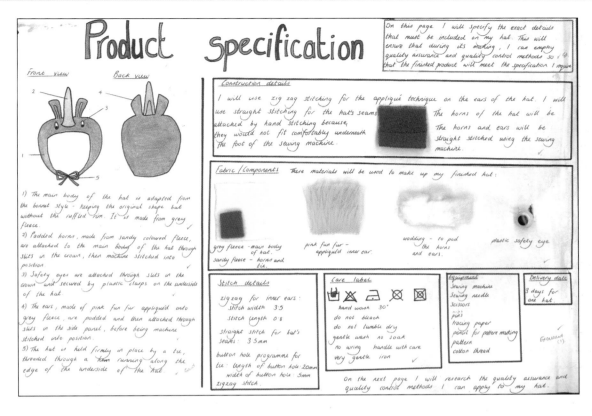

The product specification

The student work above is a good example of a product specification, in this case, for a hat. The product specification should include:

1 a brief explanation of why this page has been included and how it will help you to develop further.

2 construction details, including details for seam finishes, embellishment techniques such as batik, tie dye, etc. as well as type of sleeve or hem detail. Scan in the fabric construction method or add worked examples for visual effect.

3 a list of materials and components to be used including fibre content, weight, number of components used on the product, fastenings with measurements such as zips. Add actual examples of materials.

4 a time estimate an, ideally, details of the production method used. There should always be reference to production in batches.

5 a list of equipment.

6 care labels.

7 stitch details and machine settings. Worked examples could be shown.

8 a detailed outline of the product, including both the front and back views, dimensions or critical measurements, positioning of embellishment techniques, a brief description of each area of design and quality check guidelines. Keep the design simple. Colour is not necessary.

Activity

1 List the main points to be included in a product specification.

Key points

● A product specification details how a product is to be made.

● It is important to give full details about your final product.

The use of ICT within assessment objective 4

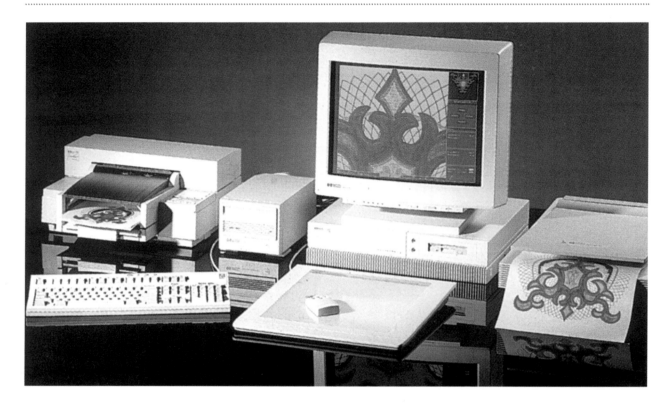

Information and communication technology (ICT) is responsible for the changes in the way in which textile items are designed and developed.

Using ICT in the classroom

ICT can be used within assessment objective 4 in a variety of ways. Hardware that could be used to great effect includes:

- digital camera – to record your testing of fabrics and components

- scanner – to scan in textiles items such as fabric samples and drawings, which can then be placed directly on your work and printed out using an A3 printer

- A3 printer – to print out your coursework profile, scanned material, etc.

Digital camera

After the initial expense, this is an invaluable tool for recording all aspects of coursework. A digital camera is easy to use. The resulting images are clear and can be imported directly into your work.

Scanner

This is an invaluable tool and has many uses other than scanning in paper images. You can scan in existing fabrics and create your own designs using natural resources such as cut fruit, which can then be printed on transfer paper and applied directly to fabric.

A3 printer

An A3 printer can give a professional look to your portfolio pages without the need for cut and paste work.

ICT can also be used for:

- analysis – with a spreadsheet package to produce charts from spreadsheets

- research – with a database package to research information on the fabrics available

- modelling – use 2D and 3D design packages to apply fabric designs to objects

- recording – use a word processing package to write up the results of fabric and component testing.

Analysis examples

Testing the suitability of fabrics

An experiment using glasspaper and fabrics can be carried out in the classroom. A spreadsheet program such as Microsoft Excel is a useful tool for interpreting, calculating and presenting data. Enter results onto a spreadsheet, highlight the chart, select Wizard and choose Chart. The results below show that acrylic fleece is the most durable fabric for a hat, then felt and velvet. Silk is shown not to be a durable fabric.

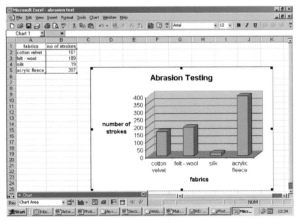

Spreadsheet showing the results of a fabric abrasion test in a bar chart

Testing insulation properties

A thermometer, containers and fabric samples can be used in the classroom to test the insulation properties of fabrics (see p.69). The results can be keyed into a spreadsheet and produced as a graph.

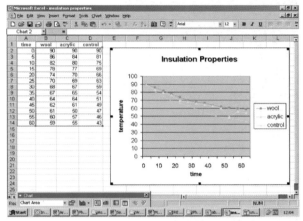

Spreadsheet and graph showing the insulation properties of fabrics

Research using a database

A database program can hold and organize information (data). Stored information is very bulky and it would take a long time to search through. A database is used to store, edit and retrieve information in such a way that it can be searched for features, characteristics and properties. A database on the range of fabrics is very useful in the textiles industry as it saves time. A fabric database in the classroom would be very useful too, reducing the number of fabrics to be tested for suitability. You could specify the performance characteristics of a fabric required for a winter hat and only those that were suitable would be selected, e.g. woollen tweed, cotton velvet, acrylic fur fabric, etc.

Word-processed tables can be used effectively to display the performance characteristics of fabrics

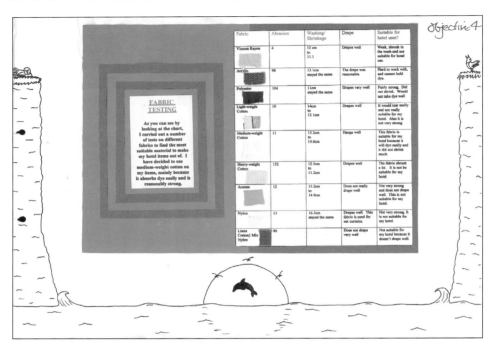

Modelling

A simple method of modelling in the classroom can be achieved by drawing an image on the computer using Paint and filling in the colours.

A more advanced but easy to operate tool is a graphics tablet with a professional software package such as Painter Classic.

A professional software package such as Micrografix can apply fabrics to 3D objects.

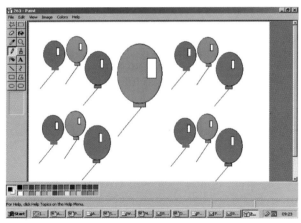

Paint can be used to fill in large areas instantly

Recording

Word-processsing can enhance work. Designs can be evaluated, tables drawn and the results of fabric or component testing entered. There are a variety of fonts which simulate handwriting (e.g. comic sans serif). The performance characteristics of fabrics can be compared on pre-prepared word-processed tables.

Activities

1 Which fabric would be suitable for children's dungarees?

2 Using a spreadsheet package, key in the following results of a fabric abrasion test for children's dungarees. Produce a bar chart to show the results.

	A	B
1	**Fabric**	**Number of strokes**
2	Cotton denim	100
3	Cotton twill	94
4	Cotton poplin	65
5	Cotton sailcloth	88
6		

3 Analyse your results and word process your conclusions.

Key points

- ICT can save time and allows you to be creative in the recommended time allowance of 40 hours for coursework (full course) and 20 hours (short course).
- ICT is a valuable tool for enhancing the appearance of coursework.

Questions

1 Towels are often made from cotton terry towelling. Explain why this is a suitable fabric. [6]

2 Give **two** reasons why weft-knitted fabrics are used for tights and socks. [2]

3 State **two** uses for warp-knitted fabrics. [2]

4 Name **two** types of knitting machine. [2]

5 Give **four** reasons why bonded fabrics are often used for disposable items such as cleaning cloths and hospital garments. [4]

6 Give **three** examples of the use of smart fabrics. [3]

7 The label in a swimwear garment indicates that the fabric it is made from is 95% cotton and 5% elastane. Explain why this blend of fibres has been used for the garment. [4]

8 The label in a waterproof jacket indicates that it has been made from a breathable fabric. Describe the advantages of using a breathable fabric for this garment. [4]

9 List **three** reasons for applying a finish to a fabric. [3]

10 Cotton fabrics used for bed linen can be given a special finish called 'brushing'. State **two** advantages and **two** disadvantages of using this finish. [4]

11 Copy and complete the lists below to link the most suitable finish to each product. One has been done for you. [5]

wool jumper   flameproof

hotel curtains   antistatic

carpet   stain resistance

outdoor jacket   anti-felting

school shirt   easy care

chair cover   waterproof

12 Fabric used for bed linen has to be resistant to abrasion.

  a Copy and complete the table below to explain how to test a fabric for this performance characteristic. [6]

Test procedure	Process
preparation	
method	
recording results	

  b Identify **two** other tests that could be carried out on the fabric. [2]

  c Explain why these tests are relevant for this product. [2]

13 The symbols shown below were found on a care label attached to a cushion cover. Explain what they mean. [6]

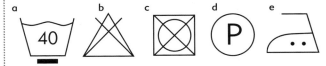

14 The illustration below shows a cushion cover.

front   back

  a Name a suitable fabric for the cover. Give **two** reasons for your choice. [3]

  b Buttons and button holes have been used as fastenings. List **two** alternative fastenings that could have been used. [2]

c List **two** other components that would be needed to make the cover. [2]

d The leaves on the design are to be worked in appliqué. Give **two** reasons why this is a suitable technique to use. [2]

e Explain how to work the leaves in appliqué. [5]

f Suggest a suitable technique to work the stem. Give two reasons for your choice. [3]

g Describe how to work the technique. [5]

15 List **four** stages during the production of a textile item when colour can be introduced. [4]

16 Tie-dye is a resist method of colouring fabric. Using notes and diagrams, explain how to create the pattern shown below. [5]

17 Explain how to screen print the design shown below. [6]

18 State **two** advantages and **two** disadvantages of roller printing 1000 metres of fabric. [4]

19 The front and back of the cushion shown in question 14 are joined using the open seam.

a Explain how to join the front and back using the open seam. You can include diagrams in your answer. [5]

b How would you neaten the seam? Justify your choice. [2]

20 Complete the table below using different examples in each case. [9]

Seam	Name	Use	Reason

21 Describe **four** ways of shaping fabric. Suggest a place on a textiles product where **each** method could be used. [8]

22 List **three** ways of neatening an edge on a textiles product. Illustrate each with a sketch and give an example of where it could be used. [6]

23 Explain the difference between basic blocks and adapted patterns. [2]

24 List **two** advantages and **two** disadvantages of using a commercial pattern. [4]

25 Identify the pattern symbols shown on the pattern piece below. [5]

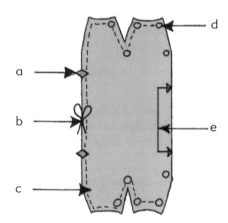

26 Explain **three** advantages of using computers to generate pattern and pattern lays. [6]

27 Describe **three** ways of transferring pattern markings onto fabric. [6]

28 Explain why it is important to make a mock-up model or a toile as part of the design development process. [6]

PRODUCT PLANNING AND REALIZATION

Tools and equipment

Examples of basic textiles equipment

Basic sewing equipment

Pins are available in a variety of sizes and can be made from steel, nickel-plated steel or brass. Some have a large glass head to make them easier to see. The type of pin used must suit the fabric and the task.

Needles are available in a range of thicknesses and lengths, and have different shaped 'eyes' and points. They need to be flexible, smooth and sharp. The type of needle used will depend on the task to be done, the type of fabric and the thread being used.

Sharps are quite long needles with a sharp point. They are good for general sewing, such as tacking and gathering.

Betweens are shorter needles with a sharp point used for fine work such as invisible hemming.

Crewel needles are medium length with a sharp point and a large eye. They are easy to thread and will take the thicker threads used for embroidery.

Bodkins are short needles with a rounded point used to thread cord and elastic through casings.

Tape measure

This needs to be made from a non-stretchy material. They are usually 150 cm long, with millimetres marked as well as centimetres. The ends of the tape measure are generally protected by metal to give a clear starting point. Tape measures are flexible and are useful for taking body measurements, and measuring round objects. If stood on their edge, they can be used to measure curves drawn on paper.

Un-picker

This is a useful tool, not only for un-picking stitches, but also to cut between the two rows of stitching which form a buttonhole.
Un-pickers come in a variety of styles but they all have very sharp blades and therefore need to be handled carefully.

Tailor's chalk

Traditionally this is a piece of chalk, usually triangular in shape, used to mark fabric temporarily. It can now be bought in the form of a pencil which is easier and cleaner to use. A small range of colours is also available to suit the fabric being marked. 'Vanishing pens' are like felt-tipped pens which either vanish after a set period of time or when water is added. Poor quality pens of this type can re-appear!

Tracing wheel and carbon paper

These pieces of equipment are used together to mark fabric. The carbon paper is available in a variety of colours and should be used on the wrong side of the fabric. The coloured coating comes off the base paper when pressure is applied, either using the tracing wheel or a pencil.

Embroidery rings

These are circular frames made from wood or plastic. The outer ring is slightly larger than the inner one, and has a screw fixed to it so that the size can be adjusted. They are used to hold fabric taut and flat, which is useful when working embroidery, quilting and some colouring techniques such as batik and painting on fabric. An embroidery ring is essential when working free machine embroidery (see p.80).

Scissors

Many different types of scissors are available due to the wide variety of tasks for which they are used. Choosing the correct scissors for the job makes it easier to complete and improves the quality of the end result. It is important to buy good quality scissors and to use them only for the purpose they were designed for.

Points to look for when choosing scissors include:

- good make and/or a guarantee
- sharp blades
- reasonably light weight
- comfortable handles
- maximum leverage for hand size
- stainless steel blades.

Minimum requirements are a pair of cutting-out shears, a small pair of embroidery scissors and a pair to cut paper. Pinking shears have a zigzag blade and are used to cut a decorative edge which reduces fraying.

Craft knife

This is a useful tool for cutting stencils, and is used with a cutting board. There are many different styles of craft knife, some with fixed blades and some with retractable blades for safe storage. Cutting boards give a slip-free surface to work on. Some have grids marked to aid accurate cutting.

Activity

1 a Name the tools and equipment below.

b Suggest a use for each.

Key points

- Buy good quality equipment.
- Choose the correct tool for the job.
- Consider safety when buying and choosing tools.

Cutting of pattern pieces in industry

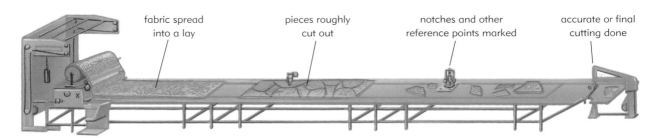

fabric spread into a lay · pieces roughly cut out · notches and other reference points marked · accurate or final cutting done

The diagram above outlines the basic cutting process in industry. Cutting can be carried out in 2 stages:

1 **Rough cutting** to separate industrial pieces.
2 **Accurate or final cutting**.

Cutting tools

There are many different types of cutting tools that could be used in industry.

Circular cutters or power shears

Advantages: suitable for cutting single ply fabrics to produce a prototype or individual garment. Good for cutting fabric plies to length.

Disadvantages: Cuts only straight lines and gradual curves only. Will only cut to a depth of 10mm to 150mm depending upon size of shears. The process has to be done by hand.

Straight knife cutter

Advantages: suitable for both coarse/ rough cutting and accurate cutting. The knife will cut corners and curves accurately to a depth of 30mm. All pieces cut from a lay are identical if the fabric is cut correctly with the knife cutter.

Disadvantages: the knife has to be controlled and pushed by hand. The process is too reliant on the skill of the cutter.

Band knife

Advantages: suitable for precision cutting to a depth of 300 mm. It will cut corners, tight curves and pointed incisions precisely.

Disadvantages: plies are stapled together to prevent slippage, therefore the process is too reliant upon the skill of the cutter to prevent mistakes. Slow production process.

An example of how fabric is prepared using a die cutter

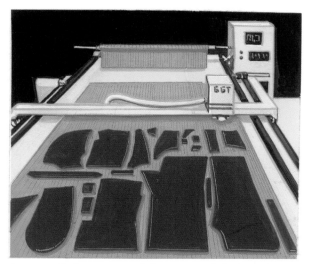

A controlled cutter used for cutting fabric in industry

Die cutter

Advantages: the cutting dies are of the same shape and size of the pattern pieces – much like a pastry cutter. These are stamped out to create identical and exact shapes. Good for use with leather, coated and laminated materials. Good for mass produced items requiring the same patterns over a long period of time.
Disadvantages: expensive to make and unsuitable for small business textile 'runs' or the formation of a prototype.

Automatic/computer controlled cutter

Advantages: fully automated so the process is accurate, fast and economical. There is a choice of cutting forms available to suit any fabric type and depth such as vertical blades, laser blades, high water pressure jets.
Disadvantages: expensive to install equipment initially.

Preparation and marking of fabric in industry

It is important that any marks or notches made on the garment to help match the pieces together exactly, are not visible once the item is completed.

There are various ways notches and marks can be made by use of:

- **drill markers** – which make small visible holes in the fabric layers. A hot drill marker may be used to make the holes more durable.
- **dye markers** – where the holes are marked by a colour, sometimes a fluorescent dye may be used which can only be detected under an ultra-violet lamp and is particularly useful for marking pocket positions and dart lengths.
- **thread markers** – where a tacking thread is stitched through the layers of fabric and is cut between each layer. A fluorescent thread may be used to give better visibility. This method is used when a drill may damage the fabric.
- a **hot notcher** – used for marking the edge of the fabric where notches may be seen on pattern pieces. Because of the heat involved this method is only used on knitted or natural fibres – the edges of synthetic fabrics may fuse together!

Once marked, the fabric has to be carefully numbered, labelled, sized and bundled ready for sewing. Every cut bundle is given a numbered ticket to ensure shades, colours and direction of pile are not mixed within a garment. These labels have to be clearly seen and not interfere with the sewing of the garment.

Activities

1 Complete your own worked example of a tailors tack and explain in flow chart form how you made it.

2 Compare the method you have used above to the use of a thread marker in industry.

3 What are the advantages and disadvantages of each method?

Key points

- use of computer aided design and construction systems in industry makes the process of garment cutting and marking easier, faster and more accurate.

Sewing machines

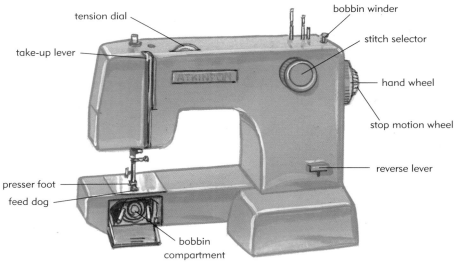

Basic sewing machine

There are many different makes and models of sewing machines available, ranging from very basic models to computer-controlled, programmable machines. Each has its own advantages.

An instruction manual will be provided with a new machine, and as each machine is slightly different, the information it provides must be studied carefully. A basic machine is shown above.

Semi-automatic machines

These machines can be set to produce straight and zigzag stitches in a variety of lengths and widths.

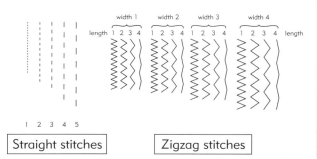

Some models allow the length and width of stitch to be adjusted independently, allowing more flexibility when working. Achieving the correct balance of stitch is important to produce a good quality result.

Automatic machines

These machines automatically adjust needle position and sequence of stitching as well as allowing for different thicknesses of fabric.

Electronic machines

Electronic or computer-controlled sewing machines usually produce a vast range of decorative stitches, including text, as well as the basic stitches. Information can be programmed in by the user and held in the memory which is supported by a battery for when the machine is not connected to the mains. The machine will set the stitch length and its width. Each model varies, some allowing the user to design their own stitches and combination of stitches, and some supplying computer disks or cartridges to extend the range of stitching.

Quality machine stitching

A good quality stitch does not pucker or snag the fabric or make holes in it. The stitches look the same on both sides of the fabric and they are all the same length. This is achieved by allowing the machine to feed the fabric through at its own rate and by using the correct needle, tension, thread, stitch length and width.

Types of needles

There are four main types of machine needle. *Set points* have a sharp point which pierces the fabric. They are used on most woven fabrics. *Ball point needles* have a rounded end which pushes the yarns of the fabric apart rather than cutting them. This type of needle should always be used on elastomeric fibre fabrics and knitted fabrics. *Cutting points* have a tip which cuts, used for fabrics such as leather. *Twin needles* are two needles mounted side by side. The two threads are connected by the bobbin thread which causes a tuck or ridge in the fabric between the rows of stitching.

Slim set point

Medium ball point

Left cutting point

The thickness of the needle is measured in one hundredths of a millimetre. Size 70 or below is considered to be a fine needle, 80 or 90 is medium and over 110 is thick. Finer fabrics need a finer needle.

Tension

The **tension** setting on the machine controls the amount of thread in the stitch. Top and bottom tension can be adjusted independently to achieve the correct balance to form a good stitch.

correct tension   top tension too loose   top tension too light

Fabric feeding systems

Most machines have 'feed dogs' in the bed of the machine under the presser foot to feed the fabric through. Some domestic machines have a 'walking foot'. The machine moves the presser foot up and down in time with the feed dog movement to feed fabric through more evenly. This is particularly useful when sewing thick fabrics or quilting.

Attachments

Some processes carried out on a machine are easier to do with the aid of an attachment; often this means a change of presser foot.

A zipper foot attachment

Overlocker

An overlocker has no bobbin; instead, cones of thread are used and threaded from the top. This machine stitches the seam, neatens the edge and trims the fabric in one operation, speeding up the making process. Overlockers are particularly useful on knitted fabrics.

An overlocker

Activities

1. Produce a sample to show the range of stitches that can be worked on your machine.

2. Produce a set of safety rules to follow when using a sewing machine.

3. Explain the uses of the parts labelled in the diagram.

Key point

- Sewing machines must be set up correctly to produce good quality stitching.

Sewing machines in industry

Industrial sewing machines are built to withstand continuous operation at high sewing speeds. They are therefore known as **high speed machines**.

Flat-bed machines are used for all types of flat sewing work. Their function is mainly lock stitch and chain stitch, although some flat-bed machines may do over edge stitching. Types of flat-bed machine include:

- *raised-bed machine* – used for fitting accessories and special attachments, e.g. button holer

- *post-bed machine* – used for sewing 3D products like shoes and bags, because of its increased height; also good for setting in sleeves

- *cylinder-bed machine* – used for cuffs, sleeves and trouser legs, particularly useful in the sewing of knitted garments

- *side-bed machines* – used for sewing edges of a fabric.

Automatic sewing machines perform more specialized functions and have special cams to control the movement of the machine components during the sewing process. An operator places the material to be sewn at the sewing position and monitors the progress.

This process is completely self-contained and monitoring systems can stop the machine if a fault is detected.

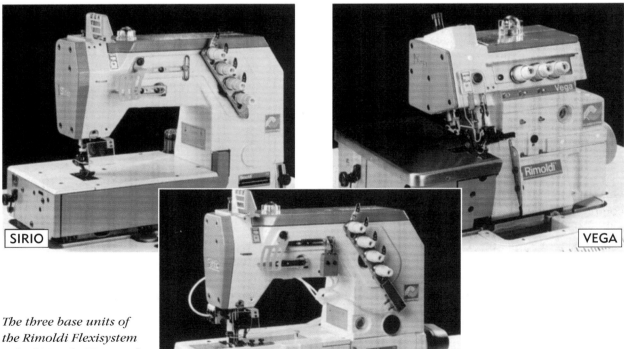

SIRIO

VEGA

FENIX

The three base units of the Rimoldi Flexisystem – the Sirio, the Vega and the Fenix. All three machines can be quickly altered and adapted to suit any fabric type and garment style

Automatic sewing machines can perform:

- various zigzag stitching patterns
- lock stitch
- chain stitch
- multi-thread chain stitch
- buttonholes
- sewing on buttons
- short seams (bar tacking).

Automated sewing machines

Types include **profile sewing systems** controlled by a template and jig. This system allows for accurate and repeatable production of components, e.g. pocket flaps, and produces items of a consistent quality. These machines may also be used for sewing the long seams on a garment. CNC (computerized numerical control) sewing machines are controlled through a computer by using either of two methods:

- *learning mode* – where the operator takes the machine manually through each step in the garment sewing cycle; the information is then stored as a programme
- *off-line programming* – the sewing cycle is digitized from a drawn pattern with exact measurements of the seam distances and then stored as a programme.

Quality is monitored continuously through the computer and any faults can quickly be rectified without holding up production. In industry the importance of fast, efficient and effective production is vital and systems need to be flexible to cope with the variety of tasks and needs. The **Rimoldi Flexisystem** consists of three base units:

- an overlock machine (Vega)
- a flat-bed machine (Sirio)
- a basic cylinder-bed machine (Fenix).

This allows it to be flexible at a reasonable cost. All three machines can be quickly altered and adapted to suit any fabric type and garment style.

Garment construction

Throughout the process of garment construction, small hand-sized manual operator terminals are used to record the work in progress and any problems that occur. Thus quality assurance is guaranteed for the customer.

The garment is sewn up in an assembly area where workers are usually responsible for a single task, e.g. stitching in sleeves. The completed pieces go into boxes or onto trolleys and are passed to the next stage.

Sometimes there are several single cell units in the factory. Here a team of workers is responsible for making the items from start to finish. This method has been found to produce optimum work output and improvement of garment quality.

Activities

A good working knowledge of sewing machine needles is important as part of a control system, e.g. light ball point needles are used for sensitive fabrics such as knits, to prevent damage to the fabric loops.

1 Find three different types of sewing machine needle. For each one, explain or show their specific features and state what fabrics they are specifically designed to be used for.

2 Explain why you think a good understanding of the different types of sewing machine needle would help a clothing manufacturer.

Key point

- Achieving a quality, marketable product relies upon:

  a the knowledge of how to set up a machine successfully for a specific purpose

  b a thorough understanding of the process of how a garment is constructed

  c the importance of having a well planned and successful control system.

Ironing equipment

An iron is a very important piece of equipment. It can be used for a number of tasks:

- removing creases from fabric
- pressing edges, pleats and seams
- setting dyes into fabric
- removing wax from batik
- fusing bonded fabrics together
- pressing folds in fabric (to remove the need for pinning).

Dry irons

Dry irons work using heat and the pressure applied by the user. An electric heating element heats the iron to anywhere between 60°C and 220°C. The thermostat in the iron regulates the temperature, maintaining it at the set level. It works by switching off the electric current when the desired temperature is reached, and switching it back on again when the temperature falls too low. It is vital that the correct temperature is selected; too hot will damage the fabric, too cool will have no effect.

Steam irons

These irons have a reservoir to hold water which is heated by electric elements to make steam. This is then released onto the fabric through small holes in the base plate. The use of steam makes creases in fabric easier to remove, and makes pressed edges crisper and longer lasting.

The water used in steam irons is significant. In some parts of the country, the water contains large amounts of calcium, which will be deposited when the water is heated, blocking the holes on the base of the iron. Some irons have been designed to deal with this, however, others require distilled water.

If the holes become blocked, steam cannot escape and the iron is less effective. These holes can also be blocked by wax and dyes, therefore a dry iron may be more appropriate for this use.

Steam irons often have a 'spray' feature which allows water to be sprayed on the fabric to dampen it. This makes creases easier to remove in some cases. Another useful feature on a steam iron is a 'surge' of steam which is released when a button is pressed. The extra amount of steam removes the more difficult creases.

Pressing equipment

An *ironing board* is used to provided a suitably shaped, stable surface on which to use the iron. The board is shaped at one end to allow small, difficult areas to be ironed.

The board is covered with padding and a layer of fabric, usually cotton as this is not damaged by the heat. Fabrics such as milium reflect the heat from the iron, conserving energy and making ironing easier.

A *sleeve board* is a smaller version of an ironing board used to iron 'tubes' of fabrics such as sleeves.

An *ironing cushion* or pressing ham is a solidly stuffed pad made used to iron difficult 3D shapes or inaccessible areas of garments.

Pressing in industry

Pressing is carried out at all stages of the process of making a textile product, in order to ensure a high quality finish. There are two types of pressing technique:

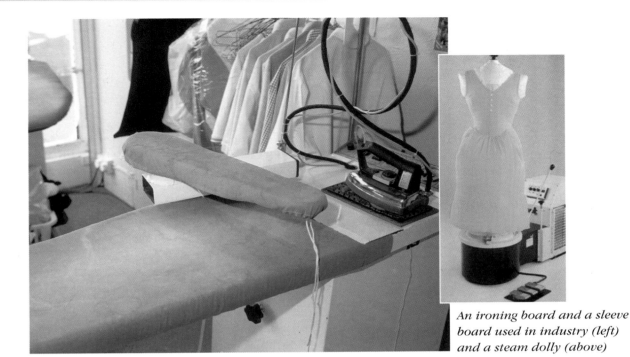

An ironing board and a sleeve board used in industry (left) and a steam dolly (above)

- *moulding* – this is a form of pressing to give shape to an area within a garment, to enhance its appearance through the cut of the pattern; this form of pressing is most effective on wool fabrics

- *top pressing* – this is the final finishing of the end garment where all parts are pressed ready for sale.

Specialized machinery is available in industry to enable these processes to be performed accurately and quickly.

The **flat press** and the **moulding press** are the most popular. Pressing is done between a buck, which remains stationary, and a movable head. The head is lowered onto the garment which is placed onto the buck. It is then steamed from above and/or below. Pressure and time used and the temperature at which it is pressed can be adjusted. On a moulding press, the buck is normally shaped like a body form.

The **steam dolly** is also popular. The final garment is usually finished with this, although smaller parts of a garment like the collar may be pre-pressed. The garment is placed over a body form which is inflated for several minutes using steam and air. The garment may also be checked and manually pressed in various areas to ensure quality, e.g. a particular seam.

The **tunnel finisher** is used in industry to press garments like shirts where they are placed on hangers and passed into a room to be steamed and dried. Manual 'spot' pressing of small parts with a steam iron may be done to improve the quality of the garment at this stage.

Activities

1 List the points to consider when choosing an iron. Identify sources of information that could be used to inform your choice.

2 Explain in detail each of the three main pieces of pressing equipment.

3 Explain why you think it is important to press a garment correctly both in industry and when making your own clothes.

Key point

- An iron is a very useful piece of equipment that speeds up making processes and improves the quality of a product.

Planning

Thorough planning when making a product is vital, both for coursework and industrial production. During product development, trialling and testing of the materials and processes needed to make the product is carried out. Information is gathered, and decisions are made on:

- materials and components, types and quantities
- processes and time needed to complete them
- tools and equipment
- possible problem areas.

The plan for making a product should include information on all of these. Cost (of materials and time) also needs to be considered. In industry, the cost of labour is an important consideration. Mass production of products will reduce both material and labour costs.

Resource requirements

Before starting to make a product, it is important to check that all the resources needed are available. A plan for making should start with a list of resource requirements including:

- type and quantity of fabrics
- type and quantity of pre-manufactured components, e.g. zips and buttons
- tools and equipment
- time available for production.

Consideration also needs to be given to demands on the resources made by others. In a classroom, tools and equipment are shared. In a manufacturing environment, more than one product could be under production at any one time.

Production schedules

Once the resources needed to make the product have been identified, an order of work can be produced. The main stages of the production process are identified first. These can then be sub-divided to give more detail. This information can be presented in a number of ways, including block diagrams and flow charts.

Flow charts

Flow charts are a diagrammatic way to show an order of work. The chart includes 'decision' symbols where a quality check could be carried out during the manufacturing process, or where an alternative material or method could be used.

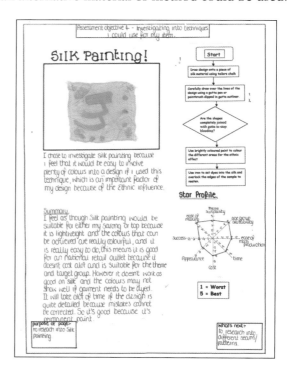

An arrow indicates the direction of flow for the tasks, and may include flow in the opposite direction if a stage has to be repeated, for example, because of a failed quality check.

Resources needed for each stage can be included in the chart. Health and safety issues should be addressed, and time allowed within the plan for safety checks on equipment, as well as sufficient time to complete tasks. Accidents often occur when workers are under pressure.

Time plans

Once the order of work has been established, the time needed to complete each stage must be estimated. This will show how long it will take to manufacture the product from start to finish.

When completing coursework, a deadline for completion will be set. The total time allowed for the project is 40 hours for the full course, 20 for the short course. The planning and making of the product is worth a little over half of the total marks. This suggests approximately 20 hours should be allowed for planning and making for the full course, 10 for the short.

If the estimated time to make the product exceeds this, it may be necessary to simplify the design, or find a quicker method for some stages. If the product will be completed in significantly less time, more complex techniques could be included.

Similar calculations apply for industrial production. A deadline for the supply of the goods will be agreed with the customer, and production will need to be planned to meet the deadline. Time plans need to take into account:

- start and finish dates
- preparation and clearing away time
- availability of tools and equipment (demands made by others using the resources)
- quality control checks
- unforeseen problems
- absence through illness
- breakdowns in machinery
- unavailability of materials and components
- health and safety.

In industry, poor planning will result in the company failing to meet deadlines and therefore losing money and business. With coursework, it is marks that are lost.

Gantt charts

This is a pictorial representation of the planned work that can also be used to chart the progress of a project. This type of chart is useful when planning activities that take place simultaneously. They show the main stages rather than a detailed breakdown of sub-tasks.

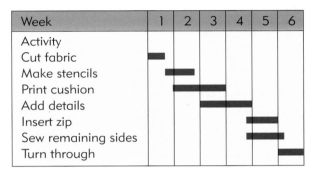

Week	1	2	3	4	5	6
Activity						
Cut fabric						
Make stencils						
Print cushion						
Add details						
Insert zip						
Sew remaining sides						
Turn through						

Team working

In industry, products are usually made by a team of people working together (see p.20). The skills of the team members should be used to best advantage to ensure a quality product in the shortest time possible.

Coursework projects can also be tackled as a team activity. However, it is important to ensure each member identifies which parts of the project they have completed for marking purposes.

Activities

1 Explain the implications for a company which fails to plan production thoroughly.

2 Identify problems which may cause deadlines to be missed.

Key points

- Thorough planning is essential to ensure a quality product that meets the deadline.
- Planning must identify all materials and pre-manufactured components needed as well as tools and equipment.
- Allowance must be made for unforeseen problems encountered during manufacture.

Ensuring a quality product 1

What is meant by the term 'quality'?

Quality can be defined as meaning fitness for purpose at an acceptable price.

What is meant by the term 'fitness for purpose'?

Fitness for purpose is defined by a range of performance characteristics, some of which are common to most textiles products, (such as durability and appearance) and some of which are particular to that specific textile product, (such as being water repellent).

What is meant by the term 'quality assurance'?

Quality assurance is making certain that a textile product meets the required specification. This is achieved through careful management of the production system. Which in turn is ensured through strict procedures from the design concept through product development, purchasing of raw materials and control of the manufacturing process to the testing and inspection of the final product. Quality assurance involves everyone working together as a team to produce a quality product.

What is meant by the term 'quality control'?

Quality control is a set of tests or inspections done at certain points during the manufacture of a product. Quality control helps to ensure that the customer is satisfied with a product.

How to ensure a quality product

The British Standard 5750 UK National Standards for Quality Systems introduced a scheme to ensure quality assurance by initiating a movement to 'get things right the first time'. The scheme involved the following requirements:

- in-depth specification details of the product to include (i) specifications of the materials used and (ii) a clear sequence of the manufacturing process and equipment used.

- checks to be made at each stage of manufacture, with materials, processes and components checked for tolerance and specification suitability.

- keeping of good up-to-date records of all test results.

If products pass the above requirements, the **BS 5750 (CEN 2900)** provides a Firm Mark for operating an efficient 'Quality System'. Registered assessors visit manufacturers to ensure the efficient  running of the scheme. Any company that is registered will have the BSI registered **Firm Symbol (ISO 9000)**.

Quality checks on the finished product are critical. At the end of an assembly line, critical measurements on each product are checked. If a garment fails, a code is used to identify the fault. If defects are not detected until the product is complete, it may have to be scrapped at the manufacturer costs.

Detailed outline drawing of the textile product

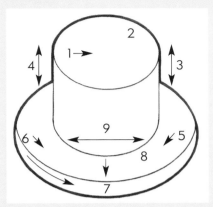

Tips

- could use different colours for numbers
- add size, dimensions and measurements
- could include different views – front, back, side
- use numbers to show parts checked – group together areas (as shown) to be constructed in the same way
- add as much detail to list as you wish, use product specification sheet to help
- do not need to add colour to sample – keep simple

Check:	Points to watch out for:
Materials and components selected	• of good working quality
1 and 2 crown of hat	• no fault evident in construction set in correctly • even gathers
3 and 4 sides of hat	• smooth seams even in size/length • seam smooth and even in width 1.5cm • set in correctly, smooth, even seam
5 and 6 base of centre panel of hat	• seam edge visible only on one edge
7 and 8 rim of hat	• even in width, smooth and of a good shape
9 decorative board	• even in width, smooth and of a good shape

There are different ways to ensure a quality outcome when making a textile product. When judging quality the following criteria might be helpful:

- the look of the item
- the fabric, yarns and components
- construction and fitness for purpose
- size
- value for money
- safety
- packaging.

It is useful to make a brief plan of all your quality checks before you start to make your product. This will provide a useful checklist whilst making is in progress (see the example above and p. 127).

It is important to add a brief summary to this section of your work, explaining how the information on the chart here will help you to produce a quality, marketable product.

Activities

1 Explain the difference between quality assurance and quality control.

2 Explain what procedures are used in industry to ensure a quality product is produced.

3 Compare two ties which are of a different quality. Look at fabric quality, construction quality, detail and features.

Key points

- A quality product will be fit for the purpose for which it was intended and it will be well designed.
- A high quality textile product is reliable in use over a long period of time.
- Product quality depends on the quality of the materials, control checks, assembly process and finishing techniques.

Ensuring a quality product 2

Quality control inspections should take place at different stages whilst making your product. A useful way to do this is to list each check point you have made next to your written plan of action points.

Remember to compare the product with your performance specification and make a decision about when to do quality checks at the different stages.

This is known as work in process and if a defect is found after each construction stage it has to be re-worked or rejected. For example, if a seam is not stitched to the specified 1.5 cm all the way along its length, it can be re-worked after inspection to give a quality finish.

It is important to check the following before making a textile product:

- When buying the fabric check that there are no faults in its construction, e.g. a pulled thread, a slub or a mark. Often manufacturers will make allowance to compensate for a fault. Be careful, look closely at where the fault is positioned.

- Ensure you have the correct amounts of all materials needed and make a list of all the sewing thread shades and numbers.

- Check that all pre-manufactured components, i.e. buttons, trims etc, are fault-free and fit for their intended purpose.

- Components that resemble foods of any type, e.g. strawberry-shaped buttons, may not be used on items made for young children for safety reasons.

- Zips are not to be used as fastenings on trousers for boys of three years old or younger.

Grading stages of a product in industry

Grade each construction stage using the following headings:

- *Acceptable quality* – the product matches the specification.

- *Rework* – the product does not meet the specification, but it can be re-worked or redone, e.g. a hem can be re-machined.

- *Reject* – the product cannot be modified in order to meet the specification so must be discarded, e.g. the fabric is torn.

Activities

1 Select a picture of a textile item in the home, e.g. a cushion or a duvet cover. Mount this picture on a piece of A4 paper and list each quality check point in its manufacture.

2 Explain why it is important to have constant checks on the quality of a textile item throughout its making.

Key points

- The quality of a product is graded after each construction stage to ensure a marketable standard of work.

- A textile product can be quality graded in one of three ways:

  a acceptable
  b needs reworking
  c must be rejected.

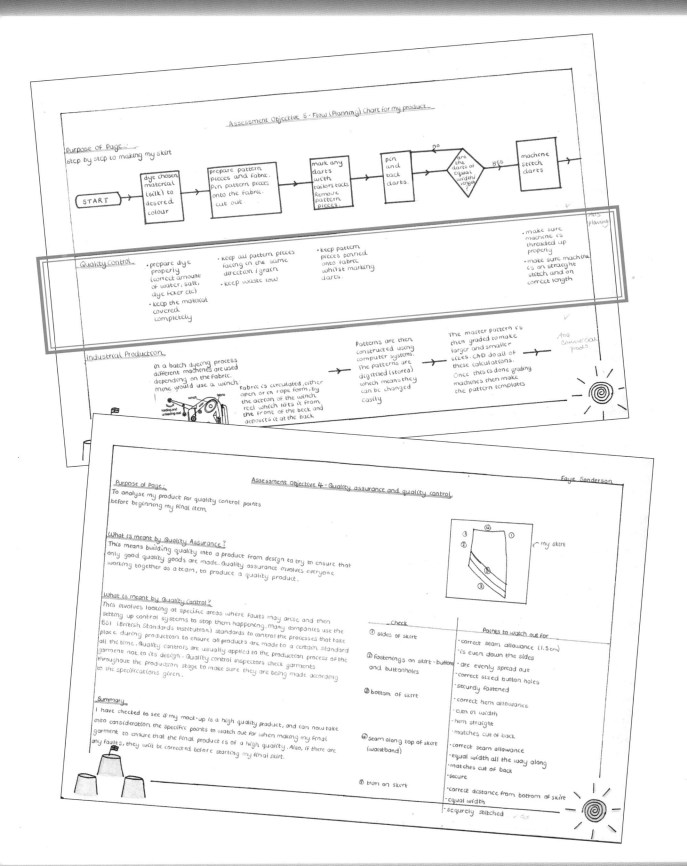

Assessment Objective 5 - Flow (Planning) Chart for my product

Purpose of Page:
Step by step to making my skirt

START → dye chosen material (silk) to desired colour → prepare pattern pieces and fabric. Pin pattern pieces onto the fabric. Cut out. → mark any darts with tailors tacks. Remove pattern pieces → pin and tack darts. → [decision] are the darts of equal width/length? — no / yes → machine stitch darts

AO5 planning

Quality Control
- prepare dye properly (correct amount of water, salt, dye fixer etc)
- keep the material covered completely
- keep all pattern pieces facing in the same direction / grain
- keep waste low
- keep pattern pieces pinned onto fabric whilst marking darts.
- make sure machine is threaded up properly
- make sure machine is on straight stitch and on correct length

Industrial Production
In a batch dyeing process different machines are used depending on the fabric. Mine would use a winch.

Fabric is circulated, either open or in rope form, by the action of the winch reel which lifts it from the front of the beck and deposits it at the back.

Patterns are then constructed using computer systems. The patterns are digitised (stored) which means they can be changed easily

The master pattern is then graded to make larger and smaller sizes. CAD do all of these calculations. Once this is done grading machines then make the pattern templates

AO4 commercial production.

Faye Sanderson

Assessment Objective 4 - Quality assurance and quality control

Purpose of Page:
To analyse my product for quality control points before beginning my final item

What is meant by Quality Assurance?
This means building quality into a product from design to try to ensure that only good quality goods are made. Quality assurance involves everyone working together as a team, to produce a quality product.

What is meant by Quality Control?
This involves looking at specific areas where faults may arise and then setting up control systems to stop them happening. Many companies use the BSI (British Standards Institution) standards to control the processes that take place during production to ensure all products are made to a certain standard all the time. Quality controls are usually applied to the production process of the garment not to its design. Quality control inspectors check garments throughout the production stage to make sure they are being made according to the specifications given.

Summary
I have checked to see if my mock-up is a high quality product, and can now take into consideration the specific points to watch out for when making my final garment to ensure that the final product is of a high quality. Also, if there are any faults, they will be corrected before starting my final skirt.

← my skirt

Check	Points to watch out for
① sides of skirt	· correct seam allowance (1.5cm)
	· is even down the sides
② fastenings on skirt - buttons and buttonholes	· are evenly spread out
	· correct sized button holes
	· securely fastened
③ bottom of skirt	· correct hem allowance
	· even in width
	· hem straight
	· matches cut of back
④ seam along top of skirt (waistband)	· correct seam allowance
	· equal width all the way along
	· matches cut of back
	· secure
⑤ trim on skirt	· correct distance from bottom of skirt
	· equal width
	· securely stitched

Product costing

It is important to consider cost at every stage of production, but particularly in product planning. Materials need to be prepared economically, allowing for waste and bought with the quality of the final product in mind. The cost of quality in industry relies on the production of marketable products at all times. These can be divided into two areas:

- cost of **conformance** – cost incurred for quality assurance (faulty goods rarely made)

- cost of non-conformance – cost resulting from errors and faults, e.g. extra inspections and testing to be paid for, down grading of faulty items to second grade, so that profit margin is lowered.

Your design specification outlines a budget you have set. Calculate material and component needs from a commercial pattern to determine the cost of your product. Consider the cost of non-conformance – e.g. if you accidentally cut the fabric with a pair of scissors. This needs to be allowed for in the calculation of your material amount. Remember to check exactly what the pattern suggests as to fabric type and amount. When presenting the costing of your product:

- explain in detail why it is important to cost your textile product realistically. Compare your ideas to the effect of cost in industry.

- list all the materials and components you have used to make your textile product.

- add the amounts and measurements by the side of each item.

- cost each item listed by adding the unit cost and then the total cost of each item, e.g. 4 x gold buttons @ 20p each = 0.80p.

- total the final cost of your product.

- include a summary statement explaining your final thoughts about the cost of your product.

- list the other factors which need to be considered when estimating product costs e.g. cost of labour, production cost in batches.

- explain how you will consider the points above when selling your product to the retail outlet and then to the consumer.

- compare the actual cost with the budget you set yourself in your specification details in assessment objective 2.

- compare your actual product cost with similar existing products. Produce a graph or chart to show the differences.

- explain your findings in detail. What is your conclusion? Have you produced a marketable product?

Costing in industry

A textile product in industry is always costed well before it is the making stage. Profit is very important to the manufacturer. Costs are calculated using two different methods:

- **Direct costs** – This covers the actual costs incurred for making the textile product. This can usually be measured accurately through the use of a computerized system.

- **Indirect costs** – This covers all the other costs that go into ensuring that the product can be made. For example, the running and maintenance costs of machinery needed to make the product, the cost of the fuel required, the payment of wages for the staff, the adverising for the product, etc.

This is why an item made by the bespoke method of production is so expensive to produce compared to a similar product made in quantity (batch) where the cost of production can be shared between each item therefore, making them cheaper to produce.

Costing of my product

I need to calculate the cost of the various components in my sarong, to find a total cost. This will enable me to work out how much it would need to be sold for, whether it is within the price range created in my specification, and whether the production method should need to be altered for manufacture in industry.

Materials used:-	Cost
White silk 1½ mtrs	£2.50
White thread	34p
Silk paints black	£1.49p (×4) = £5.96
red	(halved because ÷2
green	I only used ½ = 2.98
yellow	on sarong)
Silk outliner (Gold)	£1.79 ÷2 = 0.895
Paintbrush	2.89p

total :- £7.01

Summary statement.

Because the fabric and components cost me £7.01 to make the sarong, I will price the sarong at £14.00 this is double the construction price. One hundred percent profit is made although I must consider the fact that workers must manufacture the sarong, this includes painting on the design, sewing the fabric parts together... Some profit will go towards this.

Comparison with budget I set myself and shop prices.

In my specification, I set myself a very rough price of my sarong, to be priced between £5.00 -£15.00. When researching into retail outlets, I found the prices of sarongs to be a wide range of prices, from £6.00 to £25.00, in a wide variety of retail outlets:

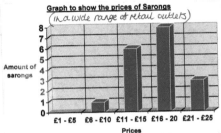

Graph to show the prices of Sarongs (in a wide range of retail outlets)

Amount of sarongs (y-axis: 0–8)

Prices: £1 - £5, £6 - £10, £11 - £15, £16 - £20, £21 - £25

Although, in the retail outlet I am targeting, 'Next' I found that prices were ranging from £14.00 to £20.00 for sarongs, few were below or above this price range.

The price I have decided upon, £14.00 is at the bottom of the range of prices of sarongs found in 'Next', I think this is a good price, it is double the construction costs but is a good quality silk sarong, a marketable product looking at the price comparisons in the retail outlet, 'Next'.

What Next? Assessment objective six

Costing of my hat

Material	Price
$\frac{1}{4}$ metre dark green fleece @ £8/metre (lining of hat)	£2.00
Remnants of red, orange, navy and yellow fleece for ears	0.40
Vilene remnants for ear flaps	0.20
Various 2nd hand woollen garments in mixed colours and items for main body of hat	2.50
Bell x 1 @10p	0.10
Poly-cotton thread x 1 reel @ 37p	0.37
TOTAL	**£5.57**

Activity

1 Using the same item that you selected on p.127 (Activity 1) for your quality control checks, list all the direct and indirect costs you think would be taken into consideration in industry.

Key points

- High quality goods are not always expensive.
- Poor quality products have 'hidden costs', such as:
  - high wastage
  - construction defects
  - inferior materials.

Health and safety

Safety in the manufacturing environment

Many potential hazards exist in a textiles workplace, whether it is a classroom or a factory. Fast moving electrical machinery, cutting tools, dyes and other chemicals can all cause injury. Workers and their supervisors have a responsibility to make the workplace as safe as possible, and to take all reasonable steps to prevent injury.

Organization of the workplace

Many potential hazards can be reduced by the way in which the workplace is laid out. Areas within the workplace should be designated for particular activities. Storage areas and walkways should be clearly marked and kept clean and tidy, with waste materials disposed of correctly. Some materials can be recycled, or a waste disposal company can be used. The area should be large enough for the number of workers, and there should be sufficient light, heat and ventilation.

Ventilation

Many processes in the textile industry generate dust and fumes. These particles in the air can be breathed in, causing damage to the lungs and throat as well as irritating the eyes and skin. The effects can be short-term or build up over time. Workers mixing dyestuffs or chemicals used in finishing fabrics are particularly at risk. Extractor fans can be installed in areas used for these processes, or the tasks can be carried out in a fume cupboard.

Storage of chemicals

Most chemicals in a work environment present a risk to health, even cleaning agents. Chemicals can be poisonous if inhaled, swallowed or absorbed through the skin. Some cause irritation or damage to the skin and eyes. Warning labels indicate the nature of the hazard. They should be stored in their original containers with instructions on how to use them.

The Control of Substances Hazardous to Health Regulations (COSHH), introduced in 1994, set out the hazards of toxic substances such as dyes, mordants and detergents, identifying which are hazardous. They detail how the substance is to be stored and handled and how to proceed if there is an accident. Before using any substance, it is important to read the instructions and follow them carefully.

Machine guards

Fingers and hands are most at risk when operating textiles machinery. Most machines have guards fitted to prevent fingers and hands being placed near moving parts. These guards often need to be removed to set up or maintain the machine, and it is important that they are correctly replaced afterwards.

Accident procedure

All workplaces should display details of health and safety procedures. This includes evacuation procedures, e.g. fire drill, and general instructions in case of accidents, e.g. where to go and who to notify. A set of guidelines for conduct and legal responsibilities is also useful.

Protective clothing

Employers in the textile industry have an obligation to provide their workers with the protective clothing necessary to carry out their jobs. Employees have an obligation to use the protection provided.

 Gloves made from fabric, plastic or chain mail: used for handling hot objects, chemicals or cutting tools

 Steel-toecapped shoes for general wear in workshops to protect feet

 Safety wellingtons worn in slippery conditions and when using chemicals

 Goggles to protect eyes, visor to protect eyes and face: used when there is a danger of splashing or flying objects, e.g. cutting

 Face masks and respirators worn when there is a risk of dust and fumes, e.g. dyes

 Hard hat for general use, to protect the head

 *Aprons, overalls and chemical suits worn to protect clothing and health, each offering increasing protection*

Risk assessment

This involves looking at the activities carried out in a workplace and assessing the risks associated with each one. Procedures or additional protection must be put in place to eliminate or reduce risk. Risk assessment covers all aspects of the workplace: layout, environment, use and storage of chemicals and tools and use of machinery.

The Health and Safety at Work Act

Introduced in 1974, the Act makes employers legally responsible for the health and safety of their employees and makes employees responsible for using the safety equipment provided.

Product safety

Many products carry symbols that indicate the product has passed a series of quality and safety tests. This is the user's guarantee that the product is safe to use for the purpose specified. The quality of materials, components and manufacturing processes used ensure the safety of the product.

Safe by design

Safety needs to be designed into a product and is often included in the specification. Fabrics and components used must be suitable, e.g. children's nightwear must be made with a flameproof finish; fillings used in soft furnishings must not produce toxic fumes if they catch fire. Manufacturing processes must also be considered. Toy parts must be secure. The end use of the product must be considered throughout the designing and making process.

Activities

1 Choose six pieces of equipment found in a textiles workshop. Write a set of rules for the safe storage and use of each one.
2 Produce a table to illustrate and explain some of the safety symbols used in the EU.

Key point

- Neglecting the Health and Safety Regulations has severe implications for both employer and employee.

Environmental considerations

The textiles industry has an impact on the environment in many ways. The main principles of conserving the environment are:

- avoiding the use of materials that damage the environment
- reducing the consumption of materials
- recycling materials.

Life cycle analysis

This is a relatively new concept that involves looking at the impact a product has on the environment throughout its life, from manufacture to disposal. Industry can identify where savings can be made in the use of materials and energy, which is good for business as well as for the environment.

Production of fibres

Using natural fibres is not always as environmentally friendly as it might seem. The land used needs to be fertilized and watered, and chemicals may be used to protect the plants and animals from disease. The chemical used in each case can contaminate the soil, water and atmosphere.

Producing man-made fibres, both synthetic and regenerated, also involves the use of chemicals, which has cost and pollution implications. Some fibres are made from fossil fuels, a non-renewable resource. Industry is reducing the impact on the environment by breeding pest-resistant varieties of plants which do not need treating with pesticides; using natural forms of pest control, such as introducing a predator; soil conservation; using computers to control fertilization and irrigation of soil; and using non-persistent chemicals (those which degrade in the environment).

Making fabrics

Making fabric requires energy to power the machines and light the factory. Noise, dust and fumes are generated. In processes such as spinning, weaving and knitting, chemicals are used as lubricants for the machinery and protection for the fibres and fabrics during the production processes.

Finishing fabrics

Finishing processes, including colouring fabric, often use chemicals. These need to be disposed of in a safe manner to avoid harming the environment. Legislation is in place to regulate how companies dispose of waste products.

Improving processes

Improving manufacturing processes will help to protect and preserve the environment. This can be achieved by reducing the amount of water, chemicals and energy used; recycling the water and heat used; using natural substances such as enzymes in place of chemicals in finishing processes; using biodegradable chemicals; regulating and reducing waste products; or by removing chemicals such as dyes from water and waste products more efficiently.

Finished goods

Finished textile products are packaged for transportation and sometimes for presentation to the consumer. Transporting goods by road, rail, sea or air generates noise and pollution as well as using energy.

Packaging has become an important issue as materials are used to make it and they have to be disposed of in an environmentally friendly way.

Washing and cleaning textiles

This requires energy, water and chemicals. Washing powders include detergents, bleaching agents and water softening agents. **Biodegradable** chemicals are used wherever possible. Dry cleaning solutions are circulated in a closed system, recycled and then disposed of safely.

Recycling textile products

Textile products can be recycled in a number of ways. Passing unwanted clothing on to someone else is the most basic method. Some materials can be shredded and made into new fabrics. It is also possible to recycle non-textile products to make into fabric. Polar fleece, for example, (see p. 62) is made from recycled plastic bottles.

Cellulose and protein fibres are biodegradable so can be disposed of in landfill. Synthetic fibres can sometimes be regenerated into a new fabric. If not, they need to be burned as they do not decompose.

Eco-labelling

Consumers are more aware of the need to protect the environment. Many are willing to pay the additional costs incurred in producing environmentally friendly textile products. Labels are being introduced to show that products have been made with minimum damage to the environment. The European eco-label is based on the vision of 'greening' non-food products all over Europe. Some people have allergies to particular materials and chemicals. For a product to have the 'Eco-tex standard 100' label, samples are tested during the production of the item to ensure it does not contain any harmful substances. This reduces the risk of an allergic reaction.

The European eco-label

The Eco-tex standard 100 label

Activities

1 Explain why it is important to consider environmental issues when designing and making products.

2 Describe the risks to the environment generated by textile production, and explain how those risks are reduced.

3 Carry out research to find other examples of eco-labels.

Key points

- The production, use and disposal of textile items have implications for the environment.

- Companies are introducing more environmentally friendly production methods.

- Consumers are increasingly conscious of environmental issues.

Questions

1 List **four** points to look for when choosing a pair of scissors suitable for cutting fabric. [4]

2 State **four** other pieces of equipment which would be found in a sewing box. [4]

3 Explain why it is important to choose the correct tool for the job. [2]

4 Explain **three** points to consider when choosing a sewing machine for a small craft workshop. [6]

5 Describe the features of a good quality sewing machine stitch. [4]

6 List **four** uses of an iron. [4]

7 Explain the advantages of using a steam iron rather than a dry iron when working with fabric. [4]

8 The illustration below shows a decorative wall tidy for a child's room.

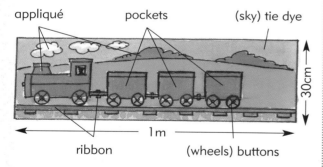

appliqué   pockets   (sky) tie dye

30cm

1m

ribbon   (wheels) buttons

a List the materials and pre-manufactured components needed to make the wall tidy. [5]

b List the tools and equipment needed. [5]

c Draw a flow chart to illustrate the order of assembly of the wall tidy. Include quality control checks. [8]

d An hour a week is allocated to make the wall tidy. Produce a Gantt Chart to show the production schedule for making the wall tidy. [8]

9 Explain **three** ways by which a company can ensure a quality product is produced. [6]

10 Explain the cost implications of ensuring a quality item is produced. [5]

11 Describe **four** implications for a company which does not produce quality products. [4]

12 Explain the implications of neglecting Health and Safety Regulations for:

a the employer [3]

b the employee [3]

13 Copy out the lists below. Link the most appropriate piece of protective clothing with each task. [4]

task	protective clothing
• using a band saw	• face mask
• checking fabric stock	• chain-mail gloves
• mixing dyes	• steel-toecapped shoes
• washing down a floor area	• safety wellingtons

14 Explain why life cycle analysis of a product can be beneficial for a company. [3]

15 Describe **five** ways of reducing the impact of natural fibre production on the environment. [5]

16 Explain how textile manufacturers can modify production systems to help preserve the environment. [6]

17 Describe **three** ways of recycling textile products. [3]

PRODUCT EVALUATION

Product evaluation 1

Evaluation against the design specification

As part of the textile technology assessment, you will need to evaluate the product against:

- fitness for purpose
- design need
- needs of the intended user(s)
- quality, with effective use of materials and resources.

It is not just the final product that needs to be evaluated – the process of designing and making also needs to be considered, highlighting problem areas and explaining the success of good working practice. This is usually called **reviewing**. In industry, a prototype product will have been made as a 'dry run' to highlight problems in the process. A number of prototypes may be used with adjustments made until everyone is satisfied with the resulting product. This is called **refining**. The aim of reviews is to improve the quality and efficiency of a system. Companies often dedicate a whole department to product modification. To structure your evaluation:

- use the bullet headings from your design specification and evaluate each one in detail using text and examples from your project as shown in the student example at the top of the next page

- use a star profile or diagram to collate your overall thoughts about your product in relation to the design specification

- produce written text, recording your feelings and findings as they happen throughout your project.

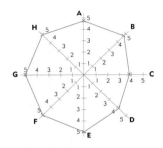

Possible specification points:

A – Suitability for target group

B – Suitability for batch production

C – Ease of making within 40 hours (20 hours for short-course students)

D – Suitability of chosen materials

E – Suitability of manufactured components

F – Suitability for chosen retail outlet

G – Overall appearance/quality

H – Fitness for purpose

(1 = worst/not successful; 5 = best/extremely successful)

How to use the star profile

Label each of the star points with a letter to match the specification points. Read the statements carefully and select the number which best fits your product and the stages in your coursework. Mark your chosen number with a cross for each statement and then join up the crosses. The more the resulting shape represents a star, the better the quality of your product and the supporting coursework.

These points should then be discussed in further detail, looking at why some aspects need improving and explaining how you could improve those areas that were least successful. It could be interesting to compare a star diagram completed by yourself, looking at how you felt your product succeeded, with one completed by a chosen 'user' of your product.

Remember to include as much detail as you can. Refer back to your market research designing and investigating sections, include the making of your toiles or mock-ups and, explain how their production was useful to the completing of a quality end product.

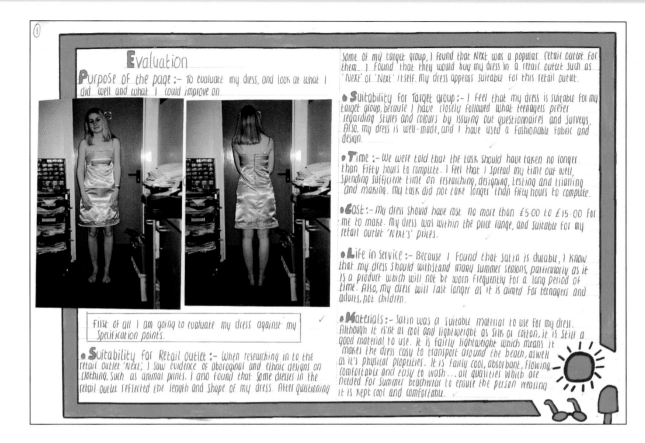

① **Evaluation**

Purpose of the page :- To evaluate my dress, and look at what I did well and what I could improve on.

First of all I am going to evaluate my dress against my specification points.

● **Suitability for Retail outlet :-** When researching in to the retail outlet 'Next', I saw evidence of aboroginal and ethnic designs on clothing, such as animal prints. I also found that some dresses in the retail outlet reflected the length and shape of my dress. After questioning

some of my target group, I found that Next was a popular retail outlet for them... I found that they would buy my dress in a retail outlet such as 'Next' or 'Next' itself. My dress appears suitable for this retail outlet.

● **Suitability for Target group :-** I feel that my dress is suitable for my target group, because I have closely followed what teenagers prefer regarding styles and colours by issuing out questionnaires and surveys. Also, my dress is well-made, and I have used a fashionable fabric and design.

● **Time :-** We were told that the task should have taken no longer than fifty hours to complete. I feel that I spread my time out well, spending sufficient time on researching, designing, testing and trialling and making. My task did not take longer than fifty hours to complete.

● **Cost :-** My dress should have cost no more than £5·00 to £15·00 for me to make. My dress was within the price range, and suitable for my retail outlet 'Next's' prices.

● **Life in Service :-** Because I found that satin is durable, I know that my dress should withstand many summer seasons, particularly as it is a product which will not be worn frequently for a long period of time. Also, my dress will last longer as it is aimed for teenagers and adults, not children.

● **Materials :-** Satin was a suitable material to use for my dress. Although it isn't as cool and lightweight as silk or cotton, it is still a good material to use. It is fairly lightweight which means it makes the dress easy to transport around the beach, aswell as it's physical properties. It is fairly cool, absorbent, flowing, comfortable and easy to wash...all qualities which are needed for summer beachwear to ensure the person wearing it is kept cool and comfortable.

Evaluation against quality

This aspect of the making process may have been considered in detail as part of the design specification evaluation. It is important to ensure that you have commented upon some of the following evaluation points:

● Success of the quality check chart in assessment objective 4 – how useful was it in the planning and production of a control system? What would you change, and why?

● What quality checks did you perform throughout the making process? Were these appropriate? How successful were they in the production of a quality outcome?

● How did you check the final quality of your garment? Was this a successful method to use – if so, why?

● Did you check the quality of existing products before making your own? Do you think this is useful in the production of a quality product – why?

Activities

1 Using one of the methods discussed in this section, evaluate two different products of the same type.

2 Explain in detail why you chose this method of evaluation.

Key points

● *Evaluation* can be defined as a process used to ensure that products match the specification criteria set.

● *Reviewing* is the evaluation of the designing and making process.

● *Refining* is making adjustments or modifications to a product based on evaluation evidence.

Product evaluation 2

Testing and trialling of a product

It is important, as the specification details suggest, 'to carry out testing, resulting in reasoned conclusions that suggest any necessary modifications to improve the product'. In industry, textile products are evaluated at every stage in the production process and to do this effectively means that each material, production method and component needs to be tested and trialled at key stages during production. This is known as continuous evaluation. Continuous evaluation helps to determine if any modifications to any process or material is required to make production more efficient and result in a better quality.

Testing can be destructive, that is, the material can be tested until it breaks or is destroyed. This is more suited to the investigations and tests done in assessment objective 4. Alternatively, it can be non-destructive – trialling is a non-destructive form of testing and is the method by which a product can be evaluated. When trialling the final product, try it out in the same or a similar environment to that in which it will be used. Use a member of the target group to trial it.

When recording your evidence you need to:

- state clearly how you intend to trial the product and why you have chosen these methods

- explain how this information will help to determine if the product is fit for the purpose it is intended for, and suitable for the intended consumer group.

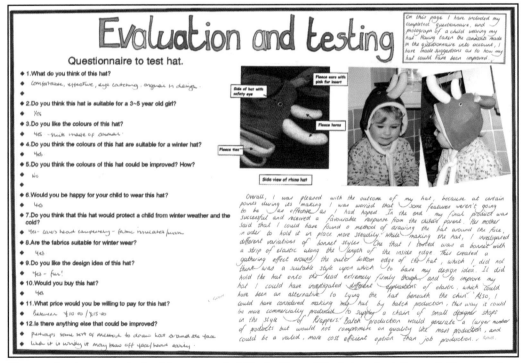

How a short-course student has recorded the testing of their product through the use of a photograph and questionnaire

Suitable trialling techniques could include taking photographs for images of the product being used in its working environment with the intended user, or writing a questionnaire or interview to find out what the target consumer thinks about the product. Useful questions include:

- Would they buy it? Why, or why not?
- What do they like/dislike and why?
- What do they feel about the price, fabric, style, size, colour, etc?
- What would they change or develop to improve the product further?

If a large number of your target consumer group is 'trialled' for their response, your market research will be more reliable. This information can then be collated and analysed using a spreadsheet or an analysis chart.

Environmental issues

When evaluating your product to see how suitable it is for the user, it is equally important to look at how suitable it is for the environment. In industry, this is one of the major concerns during production of a textile product. It is easy to assess how environmentally friendly an item is by carrying out a 'cradle to grave' analysis. This tracks the product from its beginnings as a raw material through the making stages and on to its final disposal stage after use.

Stage 1: raw material

It is not possible to take a raw material without some form of damage to the environment. However, careful management of resources can help to reduce the damage, e.g. planting trees to replace ones lost to manufacture. The use of natural fibres (as opposed to synthetic fibres) that are replaceable, recyclable and biodegradable, reduces waste disposal.

Stage 2: production process

The raw materials need to be made into yarns, fabrics and eventually textile items, so they have to go through a variety of processes that may affect the environment:

- transport of the materials to the place of production uses fuel that adds to pollution
- chemicals and energy are needed to make the fibres into fabric and the fabric into the textile item: this adds to the waste level within the environment
- recycling of chemicals and water, and extra care with insulation to reduce waste through energy/heat loss, helps to reduce damage to the environment.

Stage 3: disposal

This depends upon the life span of the product. Mostly, products are left to rot naturally although there is a significant increase in the recycling of textile goods, like clothes, through the use of collection banks.

Activities

Ask yourself the following questions when evaluating the product you have made:

1 Does the fabric you have used come from a natural source?

2 Does this mean that your product is biodegradable? Explain why this is an advantage.

3 If your product is constructed from a synthetic fibre, how could you recycle your product to reduce damage to the environment?

4 From doing all your testing and trialling investigations, what could you change on your product to make it more environmentally friendly?

Key points

- Testing involves investigating the working properties of materials.
- Trialling is the trying out of possible designs before and after making.
- Recycling of textile products helps to reduce damage to the environment.

Product evaluation 3

Control system analysis

Control system evaluation means looking at how the process of making could be improved, from pattern production through to production completion. In industry, system evaluation is usually carried out in the following way:

1 All stages in the manufacturing process, including design work, are identified/listed.

2 Problem areas are highlighted, e.g. length of time required for a dye to dry properly.

3 Assessing how problems are resolved.

4 Future improvements are suggested.

5 Alternative ways of making the product are listed, considering the following criteria:

- use of a different system (e.g. batch)

- reduction of cost (e.g. use of different materials)

- improvement of quality

- improvement of health and safety

- awareness of environmental issues (e.g. renewable sources of energy for production)

- accessibility to a range of users (e.g. culturally acceptable)

- implications for society (e.g. use of local materials and means of production).

These points are useful to help produce a detailed evaluation of your control system. The example below can help you to develop a successful analysis of classroom and industrial applications and systems. When evaluating the performance of the manufacturing control system, ensure that it is relevant and appropriate to the product you have made. Refer closely to your plan of work in assessment objective 5.

---

production system is evident – prototype made, but sarong expected to be made in batches (discuss in evaluation if correct system is used for the product)

modification to reduce cost and improve appearance – embellishment method could be done differently to reduce time and costs, increase textural interest, consistency in design and reduce risk of mistakes

Cut out with fabric scissors including seam allowances	Pin fabric pieces together, then sew. 2 Front to back using FRENCH SEAMS x2. 2 tie to front x2	Around the edges of the whole sarong, roll hem, using foot D on the computerized sewing machine	Paint on the design using the Gold Silk outliner + a paintbrush	Using different Silk paints, colour the design
Accurate cutting. Transfer pattern marking accurately	• pieces set together correctly, equal width/length. • FRENCH SEAMS sewn accurately, smooth and even.	• hem the same width all the way around.	• Use the silk outliner accurately to ensure a high quality design • Paint on thick enough so that it resists the paints painted on later.	• Do not paint on too thickly, as silk outliner may not resist thick paint, the colours will run. • Wash paintbrush frequently so that colours are kept clean.
The fabric may be laid out in one or many layers (single ply or multi ply). The fabric layers are covered with plastic and a vacuum is formed, this prevents the fabric slipping, giving a better quality cut. The pieces are cut out roughly into separate individual pieces using a computer operated blade, then they are cut out accurately. There are many different types of cutting tools: circular cutter, straight knife, band knife, die cutter, Automatic Cutter.	Components are sent to an to the factory floor, the garment is sewn up in the assembly area, workers are usually responsible for a single task, the completed piece then goes into boxes or onto trolleys and is passed onto the next stage. If there are several single cell units in the factory, a team of workers are responsible for making the item's from start to finish (optimum work output and improvement of garment quality) BATCH – Relatively small numbers of similar/identical garments, equipment and labour are then switched to another product	PRESSING is carried out at all stages throughout the process to ensure a high quality finish. QUALITY CONTROL takes place at all stages. Continual checking ensures high quality items.	Printing can be described as the controlled placing of defined areas of colour onto a substrate. RESIST PRINTING – This is when a white fabric is printed with a resist paint. On subsequent dyeing, the printed area is not coloured. Resist areas can be white or coloured.	

section showing actual step by step to making

section showing quality control points considered during making

section showing industrial step by step to making

Modification to reduce cost of the item and improve appearance

quality control considered on industrial basis, looked at in more detail in relation to production of the sarong (useful to comment upon in evaluation)

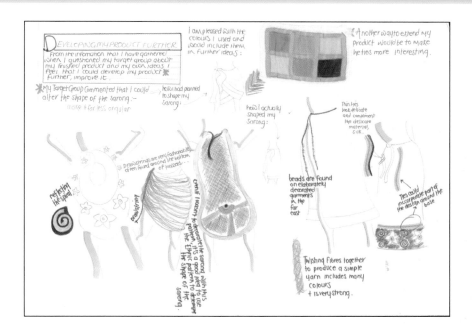

Further developments

The end statement of the evaluation needs to include at least two proposals for the product's further development, or at least one suggestion on how to modify or improve the product or the template/pattern. This could include any changes to:

- *the appearance of the product*, e.g. by addition of extra trimmings and pockets or by change to colour, style or size; for example, a jacket could be developed into a longer length coat

- *the method of manufacture* by which the product was produced (see the example opposite for ideas)

- *an extension to the pattern range*, for example to make the pattern available to a wider range of users

- *modifications to the equipment and processes* used to produce the product, for example, use of an overlocker to neaten seams and save time, compared to a flat seam with zigzag finish.

This section could be written or explained by use of diagrams or models. Some suggestions for use of ICT are:

- digitized image of the product and label

- 2D or 3D modelling techniques to show a pocket detail or style.

Activities

1 Choose a textile item popular with teenagers. Write down the reasons which you think make it popular.

2 List what you think would be suitable improvements or modifications to the product. Explain in detail.

3 Present your findings in an informative and interesting way.

Key points

- System evaluation is looking at how the production system used could be improved.

- It is useful to keep records of your progress throughout the project to help with the evaluation.

- Always consider moral, social, cultural and environmental issues in evaluating your product.

Questions

1. List the **three** areas which should be considered when evaluating a product. [3]

2. Explain how you would review the 'design and make' process. [2]

3. Why do manufacturers review and refine their production systems? [3]

4. The products shown below were designed and made in response to the following task:

   Design and make an educational toy for a pre-school child.

Evaluate each toy using a star profile as shown on p.136. [12]

5. Describe how the counting caterpillar and the baby gym could be tested and trialled. [6]

6. Suggest **four** developments or modifications which could be made to both the counting caterpillar and the baby gym. Give the reason for **each** modification. [8]

7. List **five** areas which would be included in a system evaluation in the textile industry. [5]

A counting caterpillar

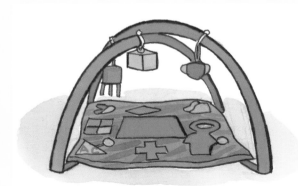

A 'baby gym' consisting of a square play mat with removable padded arches over it

There are five detachable body sections on the counting caterpillar, each with a number appliquéd on. They are joined by velcro and each section is a different colour and texture. The face is worked in transfer printing and screen printing. The machine stitching is accurate, the hand stitching less so. Woven cotton fabrics and knitted synthetics have been used to make the toy. The suggested outlet is Toys 'R' Us.

The mat for the baby gym is brightly coloured and decorated with a variety of shapes made from a range of textures which have been appliquéd on. Beads, bells, squeakers and solid shapes have been trapped beneath the shapes and inside 3D shapes. A wide range of textures has been used throughout the toy and various parts lift to reveal decoration beneath. Some parts are detachable, and some employ fastenings. A safety mirror has been included, and all of the toy is washable. Techniques used include appliqué, free machine embroidery, patchwork, quilting and a range of complex construction skills. The toy has been made to a very high standard. Woven cotton fabrics have been used for most of the mat. The suggested outlet is Mothercare.

Helpful hints to completing internal assessment

- Internal assessment will consist of a project where you will be expected to design and make a marketable textile product. A marketable product is one that appeals to the consumer and will therefore sell. This project can be linked to your own interests, industrial practice or the community.

- Internal assessment may involve an enterprise activity, where you identify an opportunity, design to meet a need, manufacture products and evaluate the whole 'design and make' process.

- If working in a group, each person must take responsibility for a uniquely definable aspect of the overall project, i.e. conducting their own research, product design ideas, manufacture and evaluation. Additional evidence is required in assessment objective 6 to show your performance and input within the project as a whole.

- You **must** use appropriate ICT to help with your work. This can include CAD and CAM software, control programs, data analysis and ICT-based sources for research. Through your project you must consider how relevant technology affects society/lifestyles.

- The textile product produced **must** be 3D.

- The activity **must not** exceed 40 hours' work (full course) and 20 hours' work (short).

- You will be awarded a mark out of 5 for the overall presentation of the project.

Key points to remember

- Use the level of response descriptors to help you to evaluate and develop your performance.

- Enjoy yourself and have fun!

Internal assessment will be marked for these assessment objectives

- Identify a need or opportunity that leads to a design brief.

- Conduct research into the design brief, resulting in a specification.

- Generate possible design proposals.

- Develop the product for manufacture.

- Plan and realize the product.

- Evaluate and test the product.

Helpful hints in preparing the project

- Although it is a good idea to protect your work during construction, do not display your work in plastic wallets for final moderation.

- Label each assessment objective clearly and ensure it is securely fastened when complete.

- Word process your work where possible, for ease of reading and presentation.

Assessment objective 1 (4 marks)

In this section, you need to identify a need or opportunity leading to a design brief for a marketable product. Look at the information on p.8 to help you structure this assessment objective. Write the task clearly and use it as a starting point for writing the design brief.

The specification states that you should provide a 'detailed description of the design need using various means of communication'. This can be done successfully in a variety of ways. Brainstorm the factors you need to consider before researching the user or design need. This initial brainstorm is done in enough detail to cover the important aspects of the design need for the short course. Once the main factors have been considered, identify the users and market for the product. These can be broken down into sub-groups.

It is important to identify the users – this can be done effectively and quickly with a questionnaire. It is also a successful way to introduce ICT into your folder work. Both full and short course students need to complete a questionnaire. A full course student may need to have more depth in their research and gathering of results for this section. Look at the student research methods opposite (top).

The idea of targeting the retail outlets is extended into another questionnaire directly targeting the user(s). If you target 10–20 people, you should be able to gather enough information.

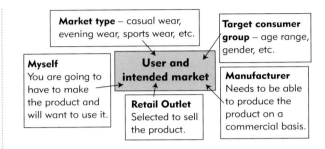

Look at the student questionnaire opposite (bottom). Notice that this student has asked a whole range of questions which allows her to evaluate the questions specifically useful to assessment objective 1, leaving the remainder to be analysed in assessment objective 2, which saves time. Short-course students should be able to gather enough supporting evidence using one questionnaire and evaluating the results. Indeed, this is sufficient for full course students, but they would be required to add more depth when justifying their reasons for selection of their target group.

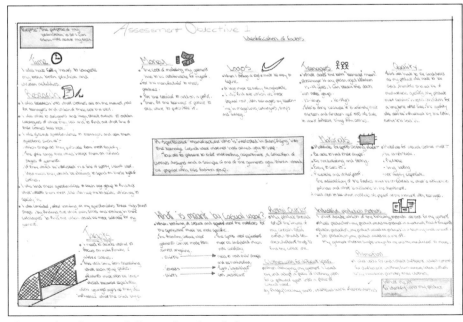

This student has carefully analysed each factor

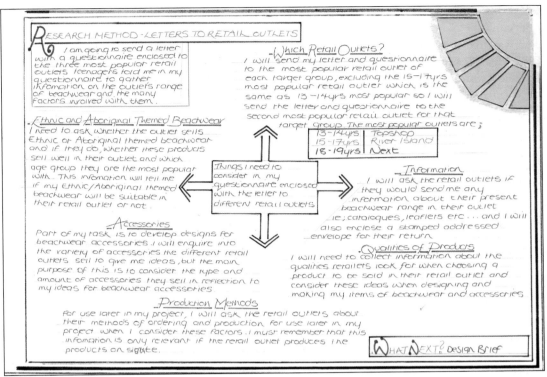

RESEARCH METHOD - LETTERS TO RETAIL OUTLETS

I am going to send a letter with a questionnaire enclosed to the three most popular retail outlets Teenagers told me in my questionnaire to gather information on the outlets range of beachwear and the many factors involved with them.

Ethnic and Aboriginal Themed Beachwear

I need to ask whether the outlet sells Ethnic or Aboriginal themed beachwear and if they do, whether these products sell well in their outlet and which age group they are the most popular with. This information will tell me if my Ethnic/Aboriginal themed beachwear will be suitable in their retail outlet or not.

Accessories

Part of my task is to develop designs for beachwear accessories. I will enquire into the variety of accessories the different retail outlets sell to give me ideas, but the main purpose of this is to consider the type and amount of accessories they sell in reflection to my ideas for beachwear accessories.

Production Methods

For use later in my project, I will ask the retail outlets about their methods of ordering and production for use later in my project when I consider these factors. I must remember that this information is only relevant if the retail outlet produces the products on sight.

Things I need to consider in my questionnaire enclosed with the letter to different retail outlets.

Which Retail Outlets?

I will send my letter and questionnaire to the most popular retail outlet of each target group, excluding the 15-17yrs most popular retail outlet which is the same as 13-14yrs most popular so I will send the letter and questionnaire to the second most popular retail outlet for that target group. The most popular outlets are;

13-14yrs	Topshop
15-17yrs	River Island
18-19yrs	Next

Information

I will ask the retail outlets if they would send me any information about their present beachwear range in their outlet ie; catalogues, leaflets etc... and I will also enclose a stamped addressed envelope for their return.

Qualities of Products

I will need to collect information about the qualities retailers look for when choosing a product to be sold in their retail outlet and consider these ideas when designing and making my items of beachwear and accessories

WHAT NEXT? Design Brief

This student has decided to target both the potential retail outlets and target consumer group to help them identify a suitable market and user

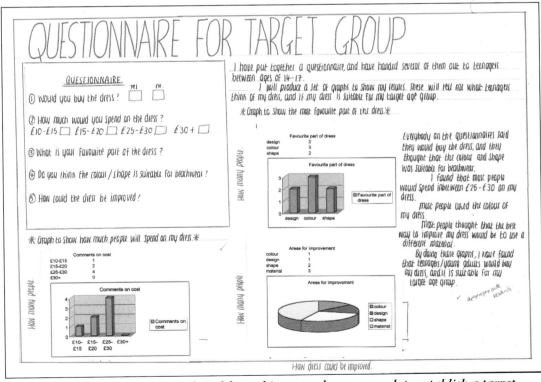

QUESTIONNAIRE FOR TARGET GROUP

QUESTIONNAIRE

① Would you buy the dress? yes ☐ no ☐

② How much would you spend on the dress?
£10-£15 ☐ £15-£20 ☐ £25-£30 ☐ £30+ ☐

③ What is your favourite part of the dress?

④ Do you think the colour/shape is suitable for beachwear?

⑤ How could the dress be improved?

I have put together a questionnaire, and have handed several of them out to teenagers between ages of 14-17.
I will produce a set of graphs to show my results. These will tell me what teenagers think of my dress, and if my dress is suitable for my target age group.

✳ Graph to show the most favourite part of the dress ✳

Favourite part of dress
design   2
colour   3
shape   2

Everybody on the questionnaires said they would buy the dress, and they thought that the colour and shape was suitable for beachwear.
I found that most people would spend in between £25-£30 on my dress.
most people liked the colour of my dress.
Most people thought that the best way to improve my dress would be to use a different material.
By doing these graphs, I have found that teenagers/young adults would buy my dress, and it is suitable for my target age group.

✳ Graph to show how much people will spend on my dress ✳

Comments on cost
£10-£15   1
£15-£20   2
£25-£30   4
£30+   0

Areas for improvement
colour   1
design   1
shape   2
material 3

How dress could be improved.

The information this student gathered from this research was enough to establish a target market and consumer group

The example on this page shows how results can be analysed in such a way that they help to formulate a clear design brief for a marketable product.

This objective is only worth 4 marks, so do not write too much; use the level response descriptors in the specification to help you. These descriptors, like the one for objective 1 on the right, are available on the OCR website: www.ocr.org.uk

Time allocation recommendations

Full-course students – no more than 4 hours; short-course students – no more than 2 hours.

Internal Assessment Objective 1 — TOTAL MARKS 4

Identification of a Need or Opportunity leading to a Design Brief	Level of Response	Mark Range
Candidates will need to:	A statement of what is to be made.	0-1
• provide a description of the design need using various means of communication;	Some consideration of the design need or the intended user/users leading to a design brief.	2
• identify the range of users and the market for which the product is intended;	Consideration of both the design need and the intended user/users leading to a clear design brief of a marketable product.	3
• develop a design brief for a marketable product.	Detailed description of both the design need and user/users leading to a clear and precise design brief of a marketable product.	4
	Total	4

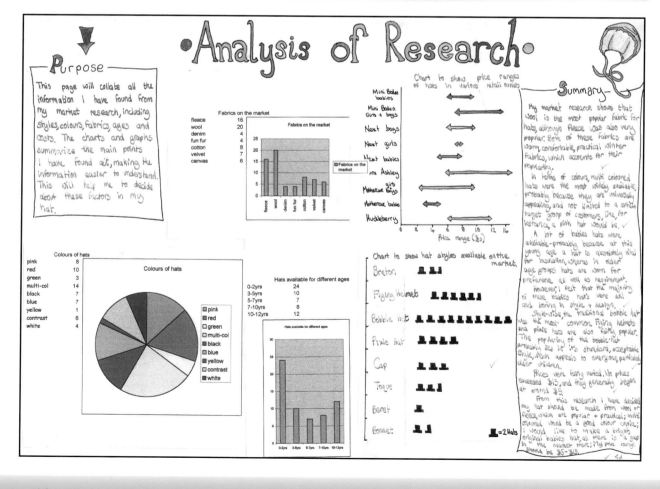

Assessment objective 2 (12 marks)

In this section, you need to research the design brief which results in a specification.

> Examine the intended purpose, form and function of the product.

This means that you need to explain why there is a need for your product and how it can be used. This can be successfully achieved through a simple brainstorm format showing: (i) how the product functions and is used and (ii) (if relevant) how the need for the product has developed throughout history.

> Undertake appropriate surveys, identifying and evaluating how existing products fulfil the needs of their intended user.

This means that you should include questionnaires, surveys or letters to help you with your market research. Do not include all your questionnaire responses in your folder work. Add an example of each type plus your results. Do not include a questionnaire if you have already completed one in assessment objective 1. All you need to do is evaluate in detail the relevant questions relating to existing products, e.g. cost, colours, styles, patterns, fabrics used. Only send letters to the retail outlets who sell the products you are researching.

Do not worry if the retail outlets do not reply to your letter. Just add a sample of the letter you have sent and state to which stores it went, and then explain what you will do instead to gather the information you want. Remember you must only include information that is relevant to the product and the user. Be selective and make sure you justify the information you include.

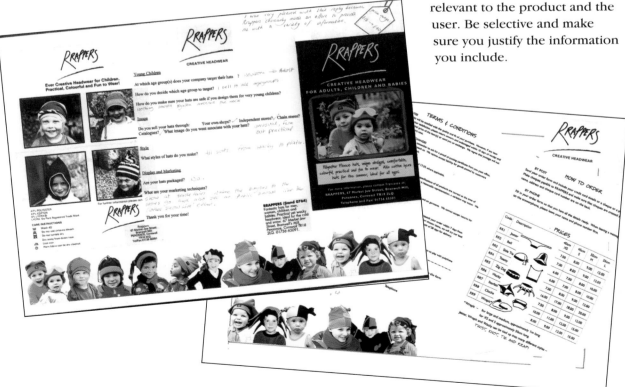

An example by a short-course student showing the analysis of a response to a designer hat outlet

The example on the left shows how a short course student studied the 'Street Scene' for existing products

The example on the right shows how a full-course student has investigated ethnic culture. Further research was done by investigating the Aborigine culture and making a choice for the product

You need to identify and collect data relevant to the product and its users. (A control system for the final product is not fully developed until assessment objective 4.) This could include research into:

- methods of commercial production
- packaging and labelling of the textile product
- display and advertising of the textile product
- cultural, environmental and safety factors
- product planning
- function of components to suit a specific need.

This example illustrates a successful way to gather and analyse results. For a short-course student this information is enough to show in-depth evaluation of existing products.

Full-course students will be expected to add more depth to this section through either assembly of products or field research into products available.

Other useful tips to remember

Include a design specification in this objective. Make sure you justify each point and explain how to produce items in batches. When cutting and sticking pictures, photographs, examples of packaging and labels into your project, do not forget to explain why you have put them there! Full-course students should spend no more than 6 hours on this section, short-course students 2–3 hours. Do not forget to use the Internet for up-to-date information. Use the mark range on the level descriptor table to help you.

Assessment objective 3 (12 marks)

This final design proposal by a full-course student gives detailed reasons for the selection of the final idea

Fabric swatches, samples of techniques and clear drawings are all evident on this sheet

In this section, you need to **generate design proposals**. You need to **generate a range of design solutions**. For full-course students, it is suggested that you produce four to six annotated design ideas, including your final design, to fulfil the statement 'a wide range of appropriate solutions'. Short-course students need to complete three detailed designs.

Each design idea should be fully evaluated against your specification points.

Present your designs with care and flair! (Do not use lined paper for designing.) There are various ways you can annotate your design proposals and link them to your specification points. Look at the examples on this page to give you some ideas on how to present your work.

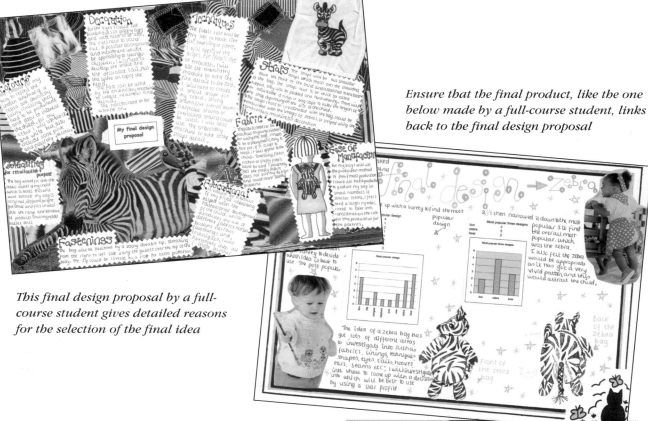

Ensure that the final product, like the one below made by a full-course student, links back to the final design proposal

This final design proposal by a full-course student gives detailed reasons for the selection of the final idea

You should always choose a final design proposal and make sure you make it stand out from the rest of your designs – add a clear title. Remember you need to give detailed reasons for the selection of your final idea and to show clearly that you have considered why there is a need for your product.

Ensure that the final product you make can be linked back to your final design proposal or manufacturing specification in assessment objective 4. Remember you need to present design solutions using a range of graphic techniques and ICT, including CAD, to generate, develop, model and communicate design proposals. For example, you could use ICT programs to add design features and pattern styles, give texture and colour or scan in fabric swatches, or you could use interesting font styles in your text to enhance your presentation.

It is suggested that full-course students spend no more that 5 hours on this section, short-course students no more than 2–3 hours.

Final product of a full-course student

Assessment objective 4 (12 marks)

This section involves all aspects of product development. The specification points out that you will need to 'as a result of investigation, testing or trialling, make reasoned decisions about materials, production methods and pre-manufactured components'.

You must show evidence of having tested and investigated materials, production methods and pre-manufactured components. You must keep all your mistakes and explain why they went wrong and what improvements you made.

You must model some part of your product in this section. This could be done by adding worked examples of the seams you have tested, examples of embellishment techniques you have tested or a completed collar or range of collars you have investigated. The whole product may have been modelled as a toile or mock-up depending upon how much time you have planned for this section and the production costs involved.

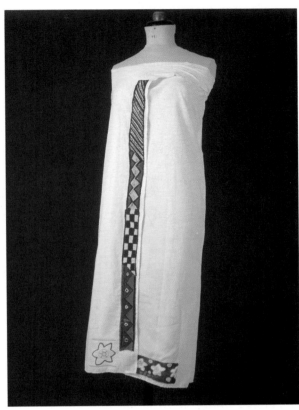

An example of a toile used to test and trial a variety of techniques, skills and processes. These tests were written up and discussed in assessment objective 4. This is often a better method of presenting investigations

An example showing how a full-course student has discussed the working of their toile and how it has been developed from an existing commercial pattern

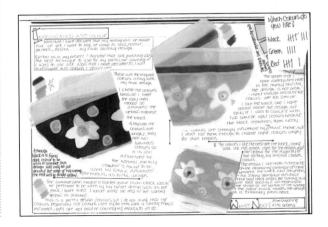

It is useful to compare only one or two different fabrics/components or methods of construction rather than spend time testing a wide range. This way you can ensure appropriate testing.

Use text books or the Internet to give your initial information about fabric/material performance characteristics to help make informed judgements about fabric or component choices. Then direct more time into testing construction, embellishment or commercial production methods. All the following areas have been covered adequately in this example:

- reason for attempting this investigation

- worked examples of each method

- comments about each method

- overall conclusions with reasoned choice.

Include discussion of how you could make the product in industry. Make this relevant to the type of product you are making, for example, if you have dyed your fabric you need to show how this would be done in industry. Give full details about your choices and decisions made in this assessment objective by using a product or manufacturing specification. Full-course students should spend 6 hours on this section, short course students 3 hours.

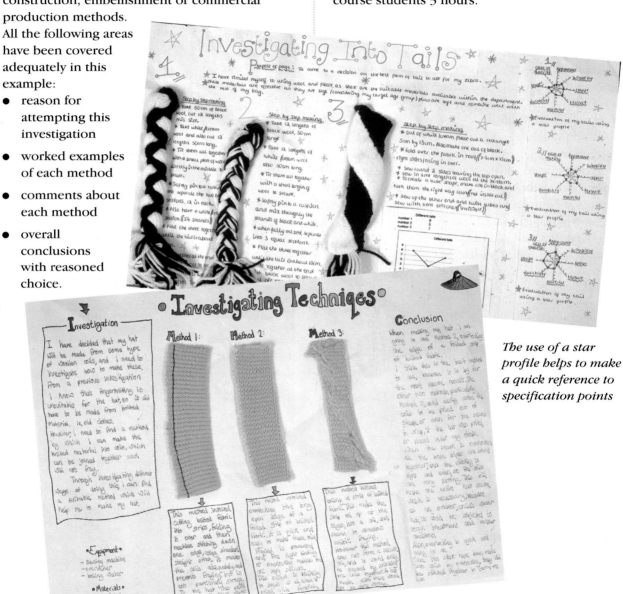

The use of a star profile helps to make a quick reference to specification points

An investigation by a short-course student into a construction process needed to make a recycled hat.

Assessment objective 5 (52 marks)

This section involves **product planning and realization**. This is where you plan and make your final product. You need to **produce a plan of action for your making** which means you need to include a flow chart showing how you will make your product step by step. You could use diagrams to explain what you will do or use the pattern instructions to illustrate how to make your textile product.

You need to include appropriate quality checks at each stage of the making process. This could be done alongside your flow chart in a different column or by using a different colour.

Full-course students should spend about 15 hours on this section which involves planning, making and costing of the product, short-course students no more than 8 hours.

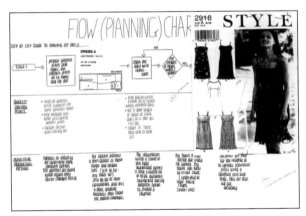

Part of a flow chart showing the use of pattern instructions, flow chart symbols, quality control checks and industrial making

You need to **select and use tools, equipment and processes effectively and safely**. It is enough to list the tools, equipment and processes you have used and comment upon why they were used and how they performed. Cost the final product and compare with your initial budget and prices of existing products. Keep all your pattern pieces to add to this section, either in an envelope or secured to a page.

Considering equipment and materials

Purpose of the page... is to look at the different pieces of equipment and materials I used and why.

Equipment used:	Reasons why:
Sewing machine	for fast, secure method of sewing
Needle and thread	for tricky details to be sewn in neatly and to sew in loose ends, initially used for tacking to hold fabric together before machine stitching
Scissors	to cut pattern pieces/material accurately and to cut off excess ends of the cotton
Pins	to hold pattern to material securely for accurate cutting and to hold material together before tacking and sewing

Material used:	Reasons why:
White fleece	to give my bag a soft cuddly feel and reflect the actual colour of the zebra, also available in the school for immediate use
Black fleece	for texture and feel, also to give a contrast to the white following the zebra theme
White/black thread	matches the fleece, suitable for invisible stitching, but also useful to give decorative detail
Zip	easy for my target group to use, cheap, available and matches the colours of the bag
Plastic safety eyes	give interest to the child and stands out on the face. Is safe and washable
Plastic safety nose	gives interest to the face and looks like a proper zebra nose, quick to put onto face, is safe and washable
Wool	easy to use and plait safely, gives a good effect and adds textural interest. Washes well

An example of a student's equipment and materials sheet

Complete a quality outcome suitable for the intended user.

Make your product as carefully as you can – it is better to make one well-made textile product of a marketable quality than to produce a range of items that are rushed in appearance and finish.

Use a range of skills and techniques appropriate to the task.

What is meant by a range of skills and techniques? Look at the example on the next page to help you.

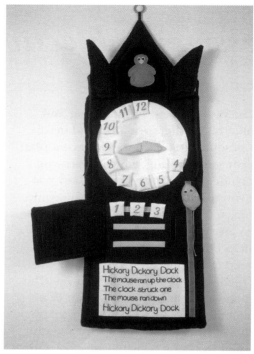

A completed marketable textile product by a full-course student

A range of **skills and techniques** has been included in the making of the playmat/hanging shown above. For example:

- Basic appliqué techniques used for
  - clock face
  - nursery rhyme square
  - insert behind cuckoo clock.

- Soft toy making used for
  - 3D mouse
  - 3D cuckoo
  - machine embroidery used for numbers on the cubes on the clock face
  - fabric pens used for writing the nursery rhyme on the clock
  - top stitching used to stitch around the edge of the mat, the door underneath the clock face and the doors at the top of the clock for the cuckoo. Velcro and ribbon fastenings included – with a curtain hook stitched in for hanging the mat.
  - soft sculpture used for clock hands and number cubes.

A range of processes have also been used:

- sewing of fleece fabric and wadding together to keep intended shape
- tacking of clock shapes onto fabric
- accurate cutting and sewing of shapes – a perfect circle has been achieved on the clock face
- securing strips of Velcro onto the fleece which keeps it straight and secure
- fabric pens – colour has not bled into fabric and writing is even and clear
- stitching of the 'hinged' doors onto the mat evenly achieved and secure
- use of ribbon – good choice of fastening, well inserted and securely attached
- top stitching even, with a consistent stitch size/length
- numbers well embroidered and equal in size.

Overall conclusion

The playmat/hanging is completed to a very high quality and has included a range of skills and techniques appropriate to the task.

Assessment objective 6 (8 marks)

In this section you need to **evaluate and test your product**. You need to **evaluate your product to ensure that it is of suitable quality for the intended user** and **carry out testing**.

You need to show evidence of detailed testing of your product. The people you test your item on should be from your target group. It is useful to combine the two statements above and use a questionnaire for your target group. This will give you a good base for a detailed evaluation.

Hickory-dickory-dock playmat being tested. A child was observed playing with the product at different stages. This information was then used to formulate valuable evaluation data

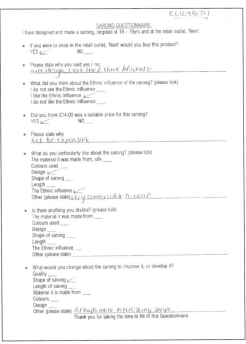

An example of a questionnaire completed by a member of the student's target group, evaluating the effectiveness of the sarong

Include photographs or scanned images of your product in use (if possible) as this is useful evidence to test fitness for purpose.

Compare your textile product with a commercially available product of the same type – looking at cost, marketable quality, appearance, size, environmental and safety issues.

You will need to review whether you have used your resources appropriately and analyse the performance of your manufacturing system. This information can easily be covered by giving sub-heads to your evaluation, using your specification points at the end of assessment objective 2. You will need to discuss each point in detail. The examples on pp.136–7 will help you.

Include further improvements/developments of your product and control system. This can be done quickly and effectively through the use of diagrams and illustrations as well as text.

Full-course students should spend no more than 4 hours on this section, short-course students no more than 2 hours.

Further developments post-GCSE

The **textile industry** is concerned with making yarns and fibres into fabrics. The **clothing industry** is concerned with the manufacture of garments. Both industries have similar job opportunities.

Overview of job opportunities

Marketing and sales

A thorough knowledge of market research techniques and the product market is required. Marketing includes the evaluation of existing products and the costing and pricing of products in relation to profit margins. This requires inter-personal skills and knowledge of a foreign language is also useful.

Advertising

Most manufacturers use advertising agencies to develop and promote the right image.

Management

A team approach to management is usual. Managers will have different roles and specialize in areas like design, product development and research, sales, marketing, human resources, quality assurance or the production process.

Design

Design relies upon market research, product research and testing and producing original ideas. Understanding the market and consumers is necessary. CAD/CAM knowledge is essential. Designers are not taught 'on the job', but need to come from a course of formal study. Many colleges and universities combine design and manufacturing studies and offer specialist study options such as textile technology.

Technical manufacture – fibre/fabric manufacture

Engineering and technical skills are needed in product development and in the installation, use and maintenance of machinery. Electronic and mechanical equipment needs a wide range of skills, especially information technology.

Textile technicians

Textile technicians operate at different levels and can attain supervisory and management responsibilities. Technicians are usually trained by companies to suit their own needs in areas like spinning and colouration.

Textile laboratory technician

Laboratory testing assesses detergents, colour, and special finishes and the impact on the environment.

Garment technology

- lay planners
- cutters
- machinists
- pressers
- packers
- examiners.

Technical jobs

Technical jobs within the textile and clothing industry include:

- specialist engineers and technicians
- technical managers
- textile technologists and textile engineers
- colourists
- buyers.

Teaching design and technology

Teaching for new entrants to the profession is usually a graduate profession. There are two routes: either a Bachelor of Education or a Bachelor of Arts/Science degree. The former is a three-year course, or four years for an honours degree. The latter involves studying for a degree in a specific subject area relevant to education and then taking a relevant post-graduate certificate in education (PGCE).

You will need the following examination qualifications to get on a degree course: a minimum of two A levels (or the equivalent) and supporting GCSE examinations which must include a grade C or above in both English and Mathematics.

Foundation and Advanced Modern Apprenticeships

There are good if you enjoy practical, vocational training methods. They are schemes linked to companies or training providers and offer high quality training following the appropriate BTec National Certificate or City and Guilds course up to NVQ level 3 alongside work experience. They are specifically suited to jobs at technician and junior management level.

Contact your school career guidance officer about apprenticeships. Use the *Job Book 2001 Springboard Careers Directory* and *Occupations 2001*.

The entry requirements for all programmes are GCSE passes in Mathematics, science and English at grade C or above, together with an additional subject at grade D or above.

Through an apprenticeship you will learn how the industry works from raw materials to the final product. Later stages will train you in a chosen occupational area, e.g. textile technician, quality testing and control, colouration, engineering or management skills. Opportunities to develop further through higher education and professional qualifications are available in many companies.

Following the successful development of modern apprenticeship schemes, the National Textile Training Organization has introduced Foundation Modern Apprenticeships, a new scheme for 16 to 18 year olds to combine full-time work and training towards vocational qualifications. The two-year programme leads to a level 2 NVQ/SVQ in textile manufacturing, sewn products or warehousing and distribution and three key skills at level 1.

Alternatively, contact **CAPITB TRUST** (The National Training Organization for the Clothing Industry), 80 Richardshaw Lane, Pudsey, Leeds LS28 6BN, tel. 0113 227 3345, www.careers-in-clothing.co.uk.

For Foundation and Advanced Modern Apprenticeship advice contact your local careers office. Information can be found through your local Learning and Skills Council.

Other routes into textile and clothing

It is usually a requirement for any clothing/textile-based course that you have a good **portfolio of design work** from school. This could be linked to work within Art or Media Studies, Textiles and Fashion, Graphics or Technology, reflecting your personal flair for design and understanding of the design process. (Courses in costume design, textile design, stage design, fashion and clothing design all specifically ask for a portfolio.)

You also need **GCSE qualifications** between 4 and 5 Grade C or above passes or **GNVQ Intermediate** to move onto **A level** study or a vocational route through a **National Diploma** and then onto a **degree course**, after you are 18. This may be broadly based or more specialized, or it may have a strong business or manufacturing emphasis, depending on the educational establishment and type of course.

Part-time courses, such as City and Guilds Fashion or Embroidery or BTec National and Higher Certificates in Fashion, are offered in areas where the clothing industry is strong.

Key points

- Visit your careers guidance officer for advice on the textiles or fashion industries.
- Check out the web sites on the Internet and career agencies for college and university courses.

Glossary

abrasion to rub or wear off to see how strong a fabric is

active smart material a material that senses and reacts to the environment

advertising to make sure a product is known to the consumer

aesthetic the way a product looks

analyse to look at a product or fabric carefully

annotation the addition of labels to a design

appliqué the attaching of one fabric onto another by using a stitching or bonding method

attribute analysis to look carefully at the different qualities of a product or material

batch production is a type of industrial production method where a specific amount of identical items are made at the same time

batik a resist form of dyeing using wax

bespoke production is a type of industrial production method where only one textile product is made

bias binding a narrow strip of fabric cut on the cross of a woven fabric

biodegradable materials that break down naturally in the environment

blend to mix together two different fibres

CAD computer-aided design

cell production is a type of industrial production method where a number of work stations are used to make one component

components part of a design

conformance the quality of a product is maintained with no or few faults

criteria a list of key words

custom a tradition

customizing changing of a product in some way to suit a specific need

denier thickness of knit

design brief design intention linked to the needs of the consumer

drape to loosely fall from the body

embellish to decorate or improve the appearance of a product

environmentally friendly will cause minimum damage to the environment

evaluate consider the success of the product

flame retardance slow down the burning process

flow line production a form of industrial production where large numbers of the same item are made cheaply

functional properties having specific characteristics

generic name a fibre's original classification

grading to size a pattern

graphic tablet a piece of equipment attached to the computer, which allows the designer to create pictures on screen using a stylus

haute couture high fashion

identify to find out or recognize the main factors/areas to consider

impregnation to saturate a fibre of fabric with a chemical or vitamin to enhance its performance or function

insulation a process used to prevent rapid cooling

interactive textile a textile that uses a microchip and conduction network together to produce a specific function

interfacing an inner layer of material used to strengthen or shape a product

just-in-time a type of industrial production method where all parts of a product arrive at the manufacturing point just in time for production to reduce costs

laminated materials that are covered in plastic

lay plan process to show the most efficient use of pattern pieces on a piece of fabric

market research to find out about the needs of the consumer through the analysis of existing products

marketing to find out from the consumer their direct needs through testing

mass production the production of a large number of items

micro encapsulation the filling of a fibre cavity with chemicals or vitamins to help increase performance

micro fibre a type of modern fibre

mixture fibres are spun into yarn and mixed together during the weaving process

niche is a gap in the market

niche marketing targeting the specific needs of a target group

off-the-peg items that can be purchased directly from the shop floor to fit the average sizes

one-off production the production of a unique product for a specific brief

passive smart materials that only sense changes in the environment

performance characteristics a way in which a fabric or material functions to meet certain requirements

performance factor how a product can react and be useful in different situations and for different needs

pilling a change in the surface texture and appearance of a fibre

pre-manufactured an item that has been completed previous to use on a textile product

process is a system of manufacture

product analysis to look closely at a product

profile (market) the use of words or pictures to describe a consumer group

progressive bundle system a method of industrial production used for larger fixed amounts of identical products

quality assurance the product must fulfil the specification points for its production

quality control tests and inspections are carried out to ensure that the product meets the specification criteria

recovery refers to a fibre or fabric and means to return to its natural shape or form

recycling to re-use textile products and fabrics

refining to improve the product through testing and evaluation

seam allowance the measurement along which the product should be sewn – usually 1.5cm

section system an industrial process used to make textile items in batches

selvedge a manufactures finished edge on a fabric

shisha an Indian technique where mirrors are embroidered onto fabric to form patterns

smart materials can sense, read and adapt themselves to changes in the environment

smocking a technique that involves the pleating and stitching of a fabric

specification (design) a list of criteria showing how a product is expected to function

specification (product) a list/set of criteria showing how a product will be made and functions

super critical fluids are added to dyes to reduce waste and help the environment

synchronized system an industrial production method used to produce large batches of textile products through a synchronised series of assembly stations

tailor tacking a form of temporary marking using a type of stitch

target group a range of people that a product is aimed at

thermo chromic dyes are dyes that can change colour when exposed to excessive heat and ultra-violet light

thermoplastic a rigid material that becomes soft and flexible when heated

thinsulate a fine fibre with insulating properties

thumbnail sketch is an initial quick sketch of the designer's ideas

tjanting a tool used in batik to place the wax onto the fabric

toile a fabric version of a pattern, which is modified/changed to get the desired look and fit

tolerance (range) the allowed variation in size or weight etc of a product

trading standards an association established to protect the consumer

working drawing a detailed drawing showing all the information needed to make the design idea

Index